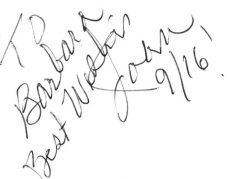

GROWING UP
IN THE
UNITED STATES
OF AMERICA

A Nurse Encounters Starvation in the Uninsured

by

Joan W. Oxendine

DORRANCE
PUBLISHING CO
EST. 1920
PITTSBURGH, PENNSYLVANIA 15238

Dorrance Publishing Co
585 Alpha Drive
Suite 103
Pittsburgh, PA 15238
Visit our website at www.dorrancebookstore.com

ISBN: 978-1-4809-5768-8
eISBN: 978-1-4809-5791-6

CONTENTS

Acknowledgments

When the Patient Protection and Affordable Care Act (ACA/Obamacare) was passed into law I was elated and so thankful that in addition to Medicaid, poor people and those who fell through the cracks because of their employment status would finally be covered with health insurance. I could not help myself by wanting to tell my story of what awful conditions and situations I had experienced taking care of the uninsured.

I want to thank my family for supporting me in this endeavor. A very special thanks goes to my husband, Bill, who has been a sounding board hearing my stories over and over throughout the years. Then he had to hear them one more time as I selected certain ones for this book. He listened to me as I read some book reference used to support certain statements. Special thanks go to Barbara Bennett and Brenda Skipwith, church members who read and edited this book. I thank my daughter, Mary, who was a reader and for her technical support. I also want to thank my pastor, Rev. William H. Lamar, IV, for reviewing the chapter on "my spiritual life." I am so thankful that God lead me to take on this task. In addition to all of my other activities, writing this book for the past two years has been a labor of love.

I have been straight forward in telling my story. I have tried not to say anything that would be hurtful to anyone. The following events are true.

Joan W. Oxendine

PREFACE

Everyone was very excited. There had been a mining accident. Uncle George had been hurt. My heart was pounding! Uncle George was my favorite uncle. Was he going to die? I asked Mother to take me to the hospital to see him. She said, "Wait until he is treated and I will take you. You are 12 years old now and will be allowed to see him." I could hardly wait. When I went to the hospital, I found Uncle George lying in bed with a huge white bandage covering the right side of his face. He could only see out of one eye. His right leg was in a cast the entire length of his leg, from his toes to his hip. It hung in a trapeze over the bed. He was able to talk and did not seem to be in pain. I was overwhelmed. I felt I wanted to do something for him. Then a white nurse came into the room of all black male patients. I thought that was strange. Where was the black nurse? I would later learn that the hospital was segregated. There were no black nurses. At that moment I knew that I wanted to become a nurse.

We lived in the city of Beckley located in southern West Virginia, a bustling coal mining region where mining accidents were the norm, not the unusual. East Park was a close-knit community of African American families. It was one of several small segregated communities in Beckley. When an accident occurred, the entire community was affected. My father was the first person I recall having a mining accident. I was about seven years old. I was excited to see him come home from work with a cast on his hand. I remember writing my name on it. (McClure G. T., 1916)

Aunt Mary's first husband, Uncle John Florence, was the victim of a mining accident and suffered a severe injury to his back that required him to be bedridden. He was in a hospital bed in the first bedroom. They were living in my grandparent's home. I was very young but I remember observing my uncle throwing a glass of urine in my aunt's face. I was confused as to what I had just seen. I ran to tell Mother what had just happened.

All of my uncles were coal miners. They all died from some form of heart and lung disease. Several were diagnosed with Black Lung Disease (pneumoconiosis). One died from lung cancer. He also smoked cigarettes. Other than mining accidents, I was not aware of other health-related issues in the men of my family. I later learned that diabetes was prevalent in my dad's side of the family.

Mother was squeamish at the sight of blood. She had difficulty pulling our teeth when they became loose. That was a big deal for her. Now, how much blood loss is created from a child shedding their temporary teeth? But that was an issue for our mother. However, she was very health conscious. She was sickly as a child having developed Scarlet Fever (and later heart valve damage) and her mother used all sorts of home remedies on her. Mother used these same remedies on her children, even though none of us was sickly. She made sure of that.

Mother was an educated and a thrifty woman. My English teacher in high school, Alyce Scott, was her classmate at Stratton High School. She often spoke of Mother as being a very smart student. In 1937 Mother attended two years at West Virginia State College located in Charleston, West Virginia (Institute). She grew a large vegetable garden every year. She canned vegetables and fruits during the summer. She was a stickler about serving a well-balanced diet. During the summer, we went berry-picking. Our next door neighbor had a cherry tree. We had four apple trees in our yard. She purchased peaches and pears from the traveling farmer who frequented our neighborhood during the summer months. He also sold buttermilk and fresh eggs. So I grew up eating and thinking healthy. However, Mother made lard-biscuits every morning for breakfast. But her focus was on making sure we ate healthy.

We only saw the doctor for injuries because we were basically healthy children. I remember us going to the courthouse to get our immunizations before school started. Dr. A.D. Belton was the family doctor who delivered all of us at home. He made a house call when my youngest sister, Frances, burned her arm while running around the hot potbelly stove which warmed the whole house. While he was there, he saw my sister, Margaret, who Mother had been treating for a "bad cold." Dr. Belton diagnosed her with pneumonia.

I do not remember my mother ever mentioning anything about health insurance. I only remember seeing her go into the trunk that was kept in the back bedroom to get money to pay Dr. Belton. That was her bank. Mother was very frugal. She was forced to be after our father deserted her and five children in 1952. I was eleven years old. My youngest brother, Dwight, was two years old. He does not remember our father.

Daddy worked as a coal miner until he left home. He was an alcoholic. His alcoholism was part of the reason for him deserting his family. There is no justifiable reason for any man walking off and leaving his five children. None. He began drinking while he was enlisted in military service.

Four of us graduated from high school. My youngest brother and I were the only two who finished college. My older sister joined the Army and had a clerical career. She attended Bluefield State College for one year prior to joining the Army. My youngest sister passed the Civil Service examination and worked in the federal government until she retired. Our older brother had a learning disability and did not graduate from high school. So, I followed my dream and became a nurse. This book will tell how I got there, what impact taking care of the uninsured had on my life, and how happy I was when President Barack Obama passed the Affordable Health Care Act.

Part One

INTRODUCTION

BECKLEY, WEST VIRGINIA

Beckley, Raleigh County, West Virginia inherited its name from General Alfred Beckley's father, John Beckley. In 1950, Raleigh County celebrated its centennial anniversary. West Virginia seceded from Virginia during the Civil War in 1863. Raleigh County was previously part of Fayette County in the state of Virginia. It is located in southern West Virginia. The counties that make up southern West Virginia include: Boone, Fayette, Kanawha, Logan, Mercer, McDowell, and Raleigh. Beckley was established in 1872. (McClure G. T., 1916)

I was born a coal miner's daughter at home and delivered by Dr. A.D. Belton, one of three African American physicians in Raleigh County. In May 1941, I came into the world and in December 1941 Japan dropped a bomb on Pearl Harbor and the United States entered World War II. I once saw ration stamps that Mother had saved. My mother was born at the end of WWI in 1918. My grandparents lived through two world wars.

Dr. Belton began practicing medicine in Beckley, West Virginia, in 1928. He graduated from Florida Baptist Academy in Jacksonville, Florida, received his AB degree from Lincoln University in Pennsylvania, and his medical degree from Howard University Medical School in Washington, D.C. He did his internship at the Freedman's Hospital, Washington, D.C. (My sister Frances' oldest child was born in Freedman's Hospital in 1966). He was the Medical Supervisor of the West Virginia Home for the Colored Aged and Infirm at the Old McKendree Hospital. It was initially built to treat injured coal miners. The hospital was segregated and composed of three wards: one for white men, one for white women, and one for black men. Where did the black women go for medical care? Dr. Belton died in November 1973. (Doctors and Dentists: Raleigh Co. Well Staffed with Physicians and Dentists, n.d.)

Dr. Belton was one of three African American physicians in Beckley. Dr. R. J. Howard set up his practice in 1921 and Dr. H. C. Hargrove in 1909. To have three African American physicians practicing medicine in Raleigh County was exceptional. There were also two African American dentists. Of course we could not afford to go to the dentist unless the toothache was so bad you could no longer stand the pain. Prophylaxis was out of the question. For that reason, my mother lost all of her teeth and was required to have dentures which never fitted properly. I would imagine because southern West Virginia was a booming coal mining region and the unemployment rate was low, the physicians and dentists had plenty of paying patients. I recall having a severe toothache which led to an extraction. During the night following the extraction my gum began bleeding. Mother did everything that she could think of to try to stop the bleeding, using pressure on the gum and ice packs. She finally called Uncle George who took me to the hospital emergency room where they packed my gum until I was able to see the dentist the following morning. Once I became an adult and was able to afford dental care, I now have a mouth full of capped teeth, a bridge, and a partial. Not like my mother who had false teeth, I have been able to retain most of my teeth.

When I was about nine years old I recall my younger sisters and brothers shedding their teeth. That was a big deal. Mother was afraid of the site of blood. Her technique for tooth pulling was to tie a cord string around the base of the loose tooth, then tie the other end of the string around the doorknob. She would get on the other side of the door and jerk the door, causing the string to pull the tooth. When I saw this procedure, I asked Mother if I could please pull the tooth. All I did was place two fingers around the base of the loose tooth and pull. Out came the tooth and everyone was happy. No dental visit required, no string around the doorknob, and no blood shed. I was the one that had the "nursing instinct." When it came to pulling teeth, cuddling my sick brother, dressing wounds, or picking sore corns on toes, I was there to help and to care for the sick and injured.

In poverty-stricken Appalachia health insurance was a rarity. Daddy served in two branches of the military; Navy and Army. He qualified for veteran benefits. Mother was a sickly child (developed scarlet fever) and Granny took extra care with her. Mother gave her children the same care even though we were not sickly. My sister Margaret was the sickest of us. She had numerous allergies and suffered from eczema. Every year during the spring, her hair would fall out. It would grow back in the fall and winter months. This happened for years. Mother took her to the dermatologist who could not give a diagnosis or even offer treatment to stop the process. Amazingly, as she became an adult, the process decreased in frequency until it stopped. Because my brother John had a learning disability and suffered from a nervous disorder, Mother gave him Ovaltine every morning to drink. I don't know what that was supposed to do. She mixed the powdered substance with milk and he drank a glass every morning. All of the children were required to take cod liver oil with orange juice every morning before breakfast during the winter months. That was in lieu of vitamins, I suppose. I developed a dislike for orange juice. I could always taste that grease no matter if there was cod liver oil or not. It took me many years to relearn to drink orange juice.

I have read several books that dealt with "folk medicine and home remedies" (Mitchem, 2007). Mother used several of those remedies on her children. When one of us got an upper respiratory infection or common cold, our chests were rubbed with Vicks vapor rub, we also ate the Vicks mixed with sugar on the tip of a spoon. The chest was then rubbed with baked onion skins. We were required to drink a "hot toddy" which consisted of lemon juice, water, sugar, and a tablespoon of corn whiskey. Then after all the chest rubs and hot drinks, we ran and jumped into bed underneath five pounds of covers. That was called "sweating the cold" out of the body. It worked.

There was mutton tallow, made from animal fats. It was a stinking ointment that was rubbed on the chest to relieve chest congestion. These home remedies were common practice in our household as it was in other African American homes. The physician was only called when the home remedies failed and the patient's condition worsened. I am happy to say that my children were not recipients of these home remedies. They were fortunate enough to have health insurance coverage. I had worked in Pediatrics for several years before either of my children were born. So I had some knowledge of what to do for a sick child.

The practice of home remedies came down through the centuries from slavery. I have not been able to prove this point, but I was told by my mother that her mother's mother (my great grandmother) was a slave. My grandmother, Ella Thomas Smith, was born in 1890. Mother told us stories that had been shared with her by Granny. She once told us that Granny said her mother told her she was a house slave. She and others would urinate in the water bucket, then put water in it for the white family to drink. She said they often spat in the food. That was their way of getting back for being enslaved. However, I would imagine that many of the folk medicine treatment that Mother practiced came from her mother who was taught by her mother who had been a slave. (Savitt, Medicine and Slavery: The Diseases and Health Care of Blacks in Antebellun Virginia, 2002)

In 1899 mines opened in Piney Creek, Wright, Lanark, and Stanford-all surrounding communities of Beckley. The New River Company built the first railway from Mabscott Junction through Beckley to Cranberry in 1906. That action caused the Sprague and Skelton mines and Cranberry and Prosperity shafts to open. Slab Fork was the first coal mines in Winding Gulf to open in 1907. (It was the birthplace of Bill Withers, the ballad singer who wrote "Gramma's Hands.") In 1915 another railway, the C & O and Virginian, built a line up to Stonecoal, West Virginia, opening up mines: Frances, Tommy Creek, Lego, Princewick, Killarney, East Gulf, Besoco, C.H. Mead, and Lillybrook. (McClure G., Letter to the editor 1916)

There was a mining boom during the 1920s until the depression in the fall of 1929. By 2010s many of the coal mines have closed. Most of the communities and towns mentioned above have become ghost towns. Many of the citizens moved away. Mechanization and fewer manpower needs were two main causes for mine closings. The coal mines have continued to close or be forced to close because of the negative environmental impact created by the use of fossil fuel and its impact on climate change. Very few young men go into the mines to make a living today. The median household income in West Virginia in 2010 was $37,600. It has become the seventh poorest state in the United States. (census, 2014-2010)

The population of Beckley was 12,852 in 1940. Beckley was known as the "Smokeless Coal Capital" as more and more coal mines opened in Raleigh County. By the 1950s the population had grown to 96,273. During this decade Beckley was a booming city; the city being surrounded by coal mining towns. On Saturdays the streets and sidewalks were bustling with people. There were so many people in town that people would bump into one another on the sidewalks. By the 2010 census the population had dropped to 17,614. The city of Beckley was literally a ghost town. Most stores had closed and moved on the outskirts of town into shopping malls. (Raleigh County Quick Facts from the US Census Bureau)

I remember as a young child the train coming up from Mabscott to Beckley where we were able to board it and ride to Quinnimont. That was a ride that included a field trip when I was in the third grade. The train no longer comes into Beckley. To catch a train, one must travel approximately 30 miles to Prince, West Virginia, taking the Cardinal headed to Chicago, Illinois, or Washington, D.C.

My paternal grandfather, Thomas (Tom) Wicks, who was a farmer, was born in Nelson County, Virginia, in 1872. Neither he nor his wife, Lena, could read or write. I could not find any historical information linking him to coal mining. The 1910 and 1920 census listed his occupation as a farm laborer. He died in Toronto, Ohio, in June of 1920 from complications of diabetes. He was listed as living in Beckley, West Virginia, according to the 1920 census. Apparently, he was visiting relatives when he died. He was buried in Toronto. Daddy was 4 years old when his father died.

My maternal grandfather, Thomas (Tom) Smith, was the son of a farmer, Jarrett L. Smith. He was born in Russell County, Virginia, in 1887. Apparently farming did not suit him or his brothers. In 1904 he married Ella Thomas from Nashville, Tennessee. Neither he nor Granny could read or write. The 1910 census identified him residing in Lipps, Wise County, Virginia. It was a small coal mining town. His sister, Vada, and her husband, Walter Jones, also lived in Lipps. Walter was a "Coke Puller."[1] The town is still unincorporated. Granddaddy was a coal miner living in McDowell County, West Virginia, in 1920. It was a booming mining town.

"McDowell County was formed from parts of Tazewell County, Virginia, on February 20, 1858. It was named after James McDowell, a member of Congress and Governor of Virginia. It was known nationally for its prominence in the coal mining industry." (Wikipedia, Mcdowell County, West Virginia, 2011). By 1900 the population in McDowell County was 18,747 increasing to 98,887 by 1950. During the decade of the 1980s the central Appalachian region lost more than 70,000 coal mining jobs. The poverty rate had climbed to 23% by 1980. The impact of the steel industry moving overseas had a great impact on the coal industry. The census data in 2010 indicated that the county's population had dropped to 22,113-almost back to the 1900 number. Today the median income for a male is $25,994 vs. $18,685 for females. The per capita income for the county was $10,174, which is the lowest in the state. (Wikipedia, Mcdowell County, West Virginia, 2011)

Mother was born in 1918 in the city of War, McDowell County. (I visited the city of War on July 2, 2016. It seemed like I was going back in time). By 1923 her father had moved to Beckley, Raleigh County, West Virginia, where he began building his house. I wondered why Granddaddy left McDowell County. After reading the book *Coal, Class and Color: Blacks in Southern West Virginia 1915-1932*, by Joe William Trotter, Jr., I since learned that there could have been

---

[1] Coke Pullers used a long bar about 5 feet to pull coke made from coal that had been burned in very hot ovens for 48-72 hours. Ovens were cooled with water before the puller could rake the coke. www.patheoldminer.rootsweb.ancestry.com/coke/

numerous reasons. Among them were low pay, housing discrimination, poor schools, and the fact that he had small children and wanted a better opportunity for them. (Joe William Trotter, 1990)

Mother, the youngest of six siblings, was five years old when Granddaddy moved to Beckley. She told us that she had little memory of McDowell County. There was Aunt Mable, Uncle Brandon, Thomas Jr., Uncle Cecil, Aunt Catherine, Aunt Mary, and one brother, James, who was born in 1907 and died in 1908 during infancy. There were several other relatives who lived in McDowell County. Apparently, once Granddaddy moved, contact with the remaining relatives was lost. After visiting McDowell County in 2016, I cannot understand why anyone would want to live there. It is located deep in the mountains. The road leading into the community is a very narrow two-lane highway. The closest city is Beckley, which is over 60 miles away. All of the mines have closed. However, the state just built a new federal prison in McDowell County called the Welch Federal Prison. The prison is about two years old.

Granddaddy had a brother, Clark Smith, and his wife, Minnie (Arminta), who also lived in McDowell County. Uncle Clark was killed at the age of 34 while working on the railroad. His legs were crushed. He left a pregnant wife and four children. I would not learn about these relatives until 2011 when I began searching my family tree.

Mother attended college for two years. Daddy had a ninth grade education. Mother worked as a domestic and Daddy worked in the coal mines. Mother and Daddy eloped in June 1940 in Giles County, Virginia. Giles County was known as the place to go for quickie marriages. Mother never told us that she eloped. I imagine after the marriage turned out so badly, she was embarrassed to admit it. To this union came five children.

All of the children were delivered at home by Dr. A.D. Belton. I was the first born. Margaret was the second child. John Franklin, Jr., was the third, Frances Mae was the fourth, and Dwight Steven was number five. I remember when he was born. We were taken to Aunt Mary's house. Uncle Willie, Aunt Mary's husband, made us pancakes. That was the first time I had pancakes for supper. Dwight was born on December 15, 1949. I thought that we were not going to have a Christmas that year. During those days a woman was required to stay in bed for two weeks after giving birth. The day before Christmas, Aunt Catherine, Mother's oldest sister, came over and cleaned the house from top to bottom. She then went into the kitchen and began baking. She made a cake and put pink icing on it. I had never seen a pink cake before. It was delicious. Uncle George bought a Christmas tree and we all decorated it the night before Christmas. Daddy was in the Army stationed in Florida when Dwight was born. I was eight years old.

Memories that I have of Granddaddy were the stories he told us about Klondike. I thought that it was a place in Beckley that I had not seen. I would later learn that it was located in Alaska. One reason I remember this story so vividly was that he would say if you were bad you would be sent to Klondike. I thought it was a bad place. One day Granddaddy and I were out back burning trash. He had given me a rag doll. That day when I picked it up there was a worm on it. I was deathly afraid of worms. I told Granddaddy I did not want to play with the doll anymore and asked him if I could throw it on the fire. He said yes, so I threw the doll in the fire. We stood there and watched my rag doll burn. As an adult I always remembered that event. I am sure my granddaddy's feelings were hurt. And maybe because I was a small child he forgave me. Another pastime as a child was playing with paper dolls. I wish I had kept one to show my daughter.

Granddaddy died in 1948 from arteriosclerotic heart disease. I would imagine breathing coal dust without the benefit of a respirator for 40 years played a major role in his demise. I recall him being sick and his bed was in the dining room underneath the only window in the room. His bed was more like a cot. I remember Mother taking care of him. When he died, the undertaker brought his body home. It was set up in the living room the evening prior to the funeral. Family and friends sat up all night with the body. This was called the "wake." I wanted to touch him, so I asked my cousin Isiah (Pig) Reeves if he would lift me up so I could touch him. When I touched him I found him to be cold and hard to the tip of my little fingers. That was a shock that I never forgot. I was six years old. Granddaddy's death certificate stated that he died from arteriosclerotic heart disease. It was signed by Dr. A.D. Belton.

Granddaddy and Granny had divorced in 1944. In the divorce papers, Granny was given a divorce because it was stated that Granddaddy was a pauper. What exactly did that mean? A 64 year old black man who had worked in the coal mines for over 40 years, no education, and in poor health. What could he do in this time of his life? He had worked hard, built and paid for his home, and bought additional property. I was appalled when I read that word on the divorce decree. That sounded like a white man's language not my grandmother's.

My grandmother died in 1947. She was 57 years old. There are only a few things I remember about her. However, Mother told me that Granny was a heavy smoker. She died of uterine cancer. Her occupation had been a laundress. That is, she took in washing for white folk. Actually, they washed the clothes and she ironed them. Her iron was a heavy cast flat iron. She had to heat the irons on a coal stove which had to be very hot. Imagine that. What a grueling task that must have been. Both of my grandparents worked very hard and endured a hard and difficult life. I often wonder what they would say if they could see their granddaughter today; a professional woman with all the comforts of life, including health insurance.

CHAPTER 1

THE ROOSTER'S ATTACK

I looked up the street and saw my daddy coming down the road in his navy uniform. I went running, jumping, and screaming to greet him. We were so happy to have him home. I was five years old.

I remember Christmas on Ninth Street. It is the only memory that I have of my maternal grandmother. She gave me and my sister Margaret little black and white polka dot dresses with a red bow at the neck. We hugged her around her neck.

While living on Ninth Street I had my first encounter with a fighting rooster attacking me. My neighbor, Betty Smith, who lived across the street, was one year older than me. We were playing in the back yard when out of nowhere this rooster came charging at us. We both ran up the steps to the back porch. Apparently, Mother heard us or she was watching out of the window. She came out of the back door with a broom in her hand swatting at the rooster. I recall us having an icebox on the back porch. The iceman would come by in a truck selling blocks of ice. I guess because of the melting ice and the drip pan, the icebox was kept on the back porch.

We lived in a duplex. There was another family, the Witchers, who lived on the other side. They had a daughter, Josephine, who was a teenager. I started elementary school while living there. Mother made me a yellow dress with a big white collar that had lace trim on it. I wore black patent leather shoes. Mother told me to watch out for the cars, look both ways before crossing the street. I walked to East

Park Elementary School, which was approximately a quarter mile from home.

We moved to my grandparent's house when I was in the second grade. Living there made my walk to school shorter. East Park Elementary School was a four room building that housed the first through the sixth grades. We had four teachers, each of whom taught two grades except for the Principal, Mrs. Glashen, who taught only the sixth grade. She was grossly obese. The children often laughed and made fun of her. When she walked, she waddled. One day one of the students drew a picture of a big fat woman on the blackboard. Mrs. Glashen came into the room before it was erased. We had a big laugh but the principal did not think it was funny.

I was always one of the tallest girls in the classroom. I was the tallest one in my household. I was often teased by neighbors because I was taller than my mother by the time I was twelve years old. I could never understand why someone would say to my mother, "You look like sisters," when Mother had a white streak of hair in the front of her forehead.

I was also teased by the children in school because I had big feet for my age. I think that I was wearing a size nine shoe when I was nine years old. Mother bought a type of shoe called "Red Cross" shoes for me that looked like little ole ladies' oxfords. I was also teased because I wore hand-me-down clothes that were given to me by the white folk that Mother worked for. Mother made me wear knee-high socks. Only one other girl was made to wear them, my best friend Cookie. As soon as I got out of sight of the house, I would roll the knee socks down to my ankles and raised them back up on the way home from school. It never occurred to me that there were folds in the knee socks that Mother could see. I did this because I was teased for wearing long socks. Today, this would be called bullying. The teasing never bothered me. I felt that the children were not Christians and therefore I would not be concerned with what they said about me. Someone once told me that "sticks and stones may hurt the bones, but words will never hurt." That statement is not true. Words can hurt. But it is all the frame of mind.

Living in Granddaddy's house was a rough life. The house did not have storm windows. Every winter Mother would winterize the house by putting plastic sheeting over the windows and strips of corking along the bottom of the front and back doors to keep the wind out. Beckley has a very high elevation, which put us up in the mountains. Winters were long, cold, and harsh. We had deep snow falls. There was usually snow on the ground from October to April some years. School was hardly ever closed. We walked to school in the snow, even when I went to high school, which was about 2 ½ to 3 miles away.

One cold winter day, when I was coming home from elementary school, I was attacked by a rooster. That was my second rooster attack. I had on legging (snow pants) and a heavy coat. The only part of my body exposed was my face. Apparently, my father was not working that day or was scheduled to go in on the midnight shift. He heard me screaming to the top of my voice and ran out to find the rooster stalking me. With the broom he swatted the rooster. The rooster was later killed but not eaten. I believe his flesh was too tough.

The house had two bedrooms, a living room, dining room, and kitchen. I never understood why Granddaddy did not build a house with three bedrooms, since he had six children: two boys and four girls. I imagine he built what he could afford at the time. (After Mother died, while cleaning out papers, I found the payment book where Granddaddy paid for the house. He paid $23.00 a month until the house was paid in full.) There was a coal stove called a "Warm Morning" that sat in the center of the dining room. The dining room was sandwiched between the kitchen and living room and the entrance to the first bedroom. The toilet was an outhouse. There was a long back and front porch. The house sat on a half-acre of land. There were four apple trees on the property: one sour and bitter apple tree, one delicious yellow apple tree, one McIntosh type apple tree, and a green apple tree similar to Granny Smith apples.

When my father was home, he and Mother slept in the first bedroom. All of the children slept in the second bedroom. There were two double beds in this room. The two boys slept in one bed and the three girls slept in the second bed. It was crowded and my oldest sister and I often fought. After my father left, Mother let the two boys have the front bedroom and she slept with our youngest sister, Frances. Margaret and I had the second bed. Finally, we had room to sleep without being crowded.

When we moved in the house, Granddaddy was still raising hogs and chickens. I remember one hog killing. The small children were made to stay in the house. But we could look out of the window. The hog was shot in the head. The men from the neighborhood came together to clean the hog. The women made a fire in a pit where they took the fat from the hog and made lye soap. We were given the bladder of the hog and shown how it could be blown up as a balloon. The city of Beckley eventually became incorporated and raising chickens and hogs was illegal within the city limits.

Once I was taken to the Beckley Ice and Feed Store by my uncle Willie during Easter weekend and allowed to choose a colored chick. The egg had food coloring injected into it before the chicken hatched. The chickens came out different colors; blue, pink, purple, and yellow. My chicken was pink. The chicken was brought home and became my pet. I was allowed to feed the chicken and watch it grow. It became a full grown hen. Mother told me one day that we would have to kill the chicken for our dinner. I cried all day because I did not want to eat my chicken. That was one of the most traumatic experiences that I remember growing up. I would not eat dinner that day.

Mother did the laundry in the kitchen using a washing machine with a hand ringer. The only indoor plumbing was a faucet that stood alone in the kitchen. She had to fill the washing machine manually. The machine had a manual ringer used to squeeze the water out of the clothes. The water was heated on the wood stove in small tin tubs. There were two large galvanized tubs that sat on a wooden bench used to hold rinse water. In one of the tubs she would put in "bluing" which was a substance used to make the clothes bright and white. There were two clothes lines that went the full length of the back yard. On this side of the yard there was no grass. On the other side of the yard was a large vegetable garden. The washing machine was stored on the back porch and rolled into the kitchen during the cold months. During the summer, Mother washed on the back porch.

Mother had a big vegetable garden and grew white potatoes, corn, several kinds of green beans, tomatoes, and white squash (which I hated), beets, cabbage, kale, collard greens, and okra. She canned most of the vegetables. During the summer the children went berry picking. I picked many buckets of blackberries and did not eat a one. I hated the seeds and till this day do not eat them. Mother also canned many fruits including berries, cherries, apples, peaches, and pears. I hated canning season-peeling peaches, pears, and apples. I hated harvesting corn. It always made me itch even when I wore long sleeves.

Mother was a good cook. She made fresh bread every morning; hot lard-biscuits. On the weekend she made hot light rolls. She would make the dough on Saturday night and store it in the refrigerator overnight. Sunday morning we woke up to the smell of baking bread. She did this on a coal stove.

I recall mother using 'Oleomargarine" to which she added coloring. The margarine was white and looked like Crisco. The food coloring made it yellow. I researched the history of this product and found it interesting that there was once a margarine war. It was created as a butter substitute by a French chemist, Hippolyta Me'ge-Mouries in 1869. Only the rich could afford butter. This created competition with the dairy farmers and a war broke out. This caused Congress to enact a margarine law which required all margarine to be taxed. In addition, the United States had a law prohibiting artificial coloring to food. Therefore, the food coloring packet was inserted into the packaging for the consumer to add later. During WWII butter became scarce making margarine the seasoning of choice because it was cheaper. This lead Congress to repeal the Margarine Act in 1957. (contributors, p. 2017)

Mother would get up very early in the mornings and make a fire in the kitchen stove. She would stir the coals in the Warm Morning and get it hot before we got out of bed. At nights she would "bank the fire." That meant putting slack (powder coal) on top of the fire. She then closed the draft, cutting off the air. In the morning she opened the draft, stoked the coals with a poker and put solid pieces of coal which burned faster than the slack. When we woke up, we would run into the dining room from a cold bedroom and stand around the stove to get warm. There was no heat in the second bedroom. We had several blankets on our bed. They were so heavy it was difficult turning over.

Coal was the source of heat in almost all homes in Raleigh County and I imagine all of West Virginia. Those who did not use coal heated with gas. Coal was inexpensive and plentiful and an excellent source of energy.

Most everyone in our community had a "coalhouse" on the back of their property where the coal was stored. The coal trucks would come down the alley and dump coal in the coalhouse. Coal was ordered by the ton or half-ton.

We had a faucet in the kitchen where we caught running water. It was not until my father left home that we were able to get a sink installed in the kitchen, a hot-water heater, a gas cooking stove, and an inside toilet. I was in junior high school. We would eventually get an automatic washing machine. The beauty of it all was the fact that the sink had two small windows over it from which you could look out while washing dishes and see the beautiful trees in the vacant lot next door.

Eventually, we sowed grass underneath the clothes line on the side of the yard where it was barren. It was a beautiful yard with two apple trees in the back yard. The garden was shortened on the opposite side where we planted grass in the front. There was a golden rod bush on the side of the hill in front of the house and a snowball bush in the corner near the two sour apple trees in the front. At last we had a beautiful yard along with the inside plumbing upgrades. We were excited and delighted, especially since we no longer had an outside to the toilet.

One day when he had been drinking, Daddy came home and was fighting Mother in the kitchen. There was a wood bin that held sticks of starter wood for making a fire that sat on the floor by the base of the kitchen stove. I came into the kitchen and picked up a piece of wood, climbed up in a kitchen chair, and came down across my daddy's head as hard as I could. His hand and arm came back and hit me, knocking me off the chair. I was not hurt, but I think I got my father's attention. I was approaching 11 years old. I was taught in Sunday school to honor your mother and father. Hitting my father was not to dishonor him but to defend my mother who was 5'3" and slim verses my dad who was 5'9" and stocky.

It was some time after that that my daddy came home one evening after he had been drinking. He and Mother had some words and he left. She was washing clothes in the kitchen and cooking dinner at the same time. He did not hit her this time. He left and did not return for several days. Mother became concerned after he had been gone for one week. She reported it to the police. I never remember the police coming to our home. One week became one month and then one year. We finally realized that Daddy was not coming back. It would be twenty-five years later that I would encounter my father.

Of course we had to go on welfare and remained on it until our youngest brother turned 18. Mother once told me that the welfare system was meant to keep individuals in poverty. She was able to work but could not make more than 80% of total income. My understanding was that the state gave her a certain amount, probably about 75% of what was needed to live. Her working could only bring the income up to 80%. If you need 100% to live, too bad. These policies leave one to do what they can to live which means getting under-the-table income. Of course to hear some tell it, welfare moms become rich. Not the case in our household. If it were not for family and the white folk that Mother worked for we would have been in bad shape.

Along with welfare came commodities. They were food handouts supplied by the Department of Agriculture and included dried milk, powdered-eggs, butter, cheese, canned meats, and flour. Mother was good at adding seasonings and mixing these items so that they were palatable.

I tell this story because I can relate to those in poverty. These are the individuals who are so affected by encounters with the health care system.

Chapter 2

A Frank Yerby's Fan

In 1953 I was promoted to the seventh grade and entered the junior high school section of Stratton High School. It was a segregated school for black students that housed both the junior high and senior high school. Black children living in Beckley were bused to school. The children living in the surrounding coal-camp communities were bused to Stratton. Many of the buses passed more than one white school to get to Stratton. The white students' junior and senior high schools were located in separate facilities.

I began high school in the ninth grade in the same building. I was a good student, making the honor roll every semester and was inducted into the National Honor Society. I knew that I wanted to be a nurse and that nursing required knowing science. So I took the college preparatory scientific curriculum which consisted of chemistry, algebra, trigonometry, geometry, and science. I was very active in the Future Teachers of America, was the Business Manager and wrote articles for the school newspaper. I was allowed to take typing as an elective because I wanted to be able to type my own papers when I went to college.

My favorite subjects were English and mathematics. My two favorite teachers were the English teachers. Mrs. Bernice Henry who taught me in the seventh and eighth grades and Mrs. Alyce Scott in the ninth through the twelfth grades. Mrs. Scott was the faculty member responsible for overseeing the publication of the school newspaper.

(She had attended Stratton as a student with my mother.) I graduated with a 3.5 GPA in a class of 120 students. I was fourth in the class.

When I was 16 years old I applied for a summer job as a clerk at the G.C. Murphy (five-and dime department store) in Beckley. I filled out an application and was allowed to take a simple math test. I never heard a word from their human resources personnel. Mother and I came to the conclusion that as soon as I walked out of the office my application was thrown into the trash can. It was not that I did not pass the math test, I was making straight A's in all of my math classes in high school. One day Mother and I were in the store shortly after I submitted my application. Mother was purchasing some Fig Newton cookies, which she loved. The clerk was counting on her fingers to add up the total. She apparently ran out of fingers and had to resort to writing the numbers on a pink slip of paper. I immediately told her how much the purchase was and called her dumb. Mother became very upset and told me I could not speak to that white girl like that. The store would rather hire a dumb white girl than a smart black one. I never forgot that incident.

I suffered from severely painful menstruation (dysmenorrhea). The pain caused me to lose at least one day of school almost every month. It was so severe that I would become nauseated, vomit, and develop diarrhea. My abdomen was so tender that I could barely stand for the elastic on my underwear to touch my skin. Mother would purchase some kind of tonic from the "Traveling Medicine Man." The tonic was black in color and had an awful taste. I would gag at the thoughts of taking it. The tonic had to be taken several days prior to menstruation. I thought if I did not take this awful medicine, my pain would be worse. Even after drinking the liquid, I still suffered pain. Once while in school, I fainted due to severe pain. One of the school staff personnel took me home. Mother came home from work and called Dr. Belton. He made a house call and gave me an injection. It knocked me out. He left a few pills and told Mother they could not be refilled because they were habit forming.

Stratton High School was established from the Rock Quarry School in 1907. In 1909 the school was moved to Fayette Street and was an elementary school. Throughout the years additional classes were added and in 1926 it graduated its first high school class. My mother graduated from the high school in 1937. All of her siblings did as well.

The passage of the 1965 Civil Rights Act and integration led to the closure of Stratton in 1967. The high school where white students went, Woodrow Wilson High School, was also closed. The city of Beckley had a new high school built which should have been named Beckley High School. Instead, the school was given the name, Woodrow Wilson High School. The old Woodrow Wilson High School was renamed Beckley Junior High School. Stratton High School was renamed Stratton Elementary. What the white people were doing with this action was making sure that the white alumni always had a Woodrow Wilson High School alma mater. The African American graduates had nothing. They graduated from Stratton High School, not Stratton Elementary School. The white people's thinking and actions were selfish and discriminatory. Furthermore, those who graduated from Woodrow Wilson High School prior to 1967 have no allegiance to the new school. They never walked the hallways nor sat in the new classroom. They did not enjoy seeing football games on the field. So what are they coming back to?

Stratton High School had a faculty of twenty teachers. All had a minimum of a bachelor's degree with additional hours. Seven of the teachers held Masters Degrees. They were Mr. Vance Bland: science teacher, Master of Education; Roy Dawson: Masters of Mathematics, Alyce Scott: Masters in English; Jewell Green: English and Science, Masters of Education; Bernice Henry: English, Masters of Arts; and Hallye Jeffries: English, Masters of Arts. Some went to historically black colleges and some attended white universities and colleges. I believe that students graduating from Stratton High School had a solid secondary education.

During the summer months I spent a lot of time in the public library. Because our family was poor, we did not have the luxury of going to summer camp. We did not have any close relatives or grandparents to visit who lived out-of-state. So, I occupied myself by reading. I would bring about 10 or 12 books home from the library and within two weeks I would have read them all. Initially, my favorite writer was Zane Grey. I loved reading about western pioneers and wagon trains moving westward. I would get absorbed in the novels, especially when the fighting began as the families moved across the rural plains and undeveloped lands. Reading about the Indian's land being taken was very unsettling. I would have long conversations with Mother about this.

My next great love was Earl Stanley Gardner. I loved mysteries. I read every novel published at that time about Perry Mason. When the Perry Mason series came on television, I had read many of the stories.

As I became older, my taste changed and I found a novel written by Frank Yerby. He wrote about beautiful women and their lives in New Orleans during the 19th century. I read every novel he wrote never knowing that he was African American. *The Foxes of Harrow* was the first novel that I read. I could not put the book down. I fell in love with Frank Yerby's novels. It was many years later that I learned he was one of the first African American writers whose work was produced into a Hollywood movie. Of course, I went to see the movie, Foxes of Harrow. It was nothing like the book, which is often the case.

My best friend, Cookie (Mary) Pearson, had an older sister named Edna who was about 18 years old. She read true love-story magazines. When I went to visit Cookie, out of her mother's view, we would read some of the magazines. We would read and giggle when we saw the word SEX. We thought that was a bad word and that we should not have been reading the magazines. How funny it was thinking about it later in life. I am sure Cookie got some big laughs, too.

My other pastime was listening to the radio. I had my own radio Daddy had given to me as a Christmas present before he left home. I was probably about nine or ten years old. I had a special place in the living room where my radio sat. I would stand by the table and put my ear right on the front of the radio and disappear from what was going on in my house. Family members would be calling me and I would not hear them because I was caught up in a scene that I was hearing. The radio had programs such as "Johnny Dollar" who was an insurance investigator. Then there was "Inspector Hearthstone of the Death Squad" which was one of my favorite mysteries in addition to "The Shadow Knows." Of course "Gun Smoke" and "Amos and Andy" were favorites too. When Amos and Andy came on television I was happy to see that they were African Americans. It wasn't until the NAACP complained that the show was belittling the race that it was subsequently taken off the air. I kept the radio until I left home at the age of 18.

I was 15 years old when we got our first television. That meant we didn't have to go over to Aunt Mary and Uncle Willie's house to watch television. We were required to complete our homework every evening before going to bed. We were allowed to watch television only on Friday and Saturday evenings and Sunday afternoon.

My brother John Jr. had a learning disability. He was slow in learning his numbers and how to read. In those days, there were no Special Education programs. Mother was his special education teacher. She spent hours and hours with him going over, and over and over simple words like "the," "this," and "that." She spent hours teaching him how to count money. She finally decided that if she could teach him to sign his name and count money that would help him through life.

Mother was instrumental in getting him into the Upward Bound Program, a training program for youths with learning disabilities. He was trained to work in a dry cleaners. After he completed the training, he never worked a day in a cleaners. He would eventually work as a porter. The one difficulty that all of us had and still have with our brother is that he is dishonest. He will steal and lie at the blink of an eye. You, still to this day, cannot believe anything that he says. That character trait has nothing to do with having a learning disability. He would eventually get married and father three sons, all of whom turned out to be normal, healthy, and wonderful sons. He and his wife divorced sometime later.

I graduated in 1959. Stratton High School closed in 1967. School reunions are held every other year and include everyone who ever attended the school from 1909 to 1967. I see upper classmen and women who were five years older than me. One classmate is Bill Withers[2]. Some played sports and other activities. We had a Thespian club and Glee club.

[2] Sings the ballads "Grandma's Hands," "Lovely Day," and "Lean on Me."

I had no idea how I was going to college or nursing school after high school. Mother was working as a domestic and we were on Aid for Dependent Children (welfare). Even though my uncles worked in the coal mines and made good salaries; none ever had a conversation with me about sending or helping me go to school.

Three of my mother's siblings owned their own homes. Uncle Cecil was Mother's older brother. He lived one street over from us. Initially he and his family lived in a small shingle-siding house. He later had a brick house built across the street. He married Lettie Burnett who was a widow with four children. They were Horace, Burdiss, Joyce, and Eugene (Jeepy). Jeepy was four years old when his mother married my uncle. He and Aunt Lettie never had any children together. Uncle Cecil was not a kind stepfather. He put a roof over their heads, fed and clothed them. But his interactions with them were not fatherly. As soon as the children finished high school they left home and came back very seldom, only briefly to see their mother. Uncle Cecil was mean spirited. Mother often told us stories of how Uncle Cecil was mean to her and Aunt Mary when they were young girls.

One story she told was when they had attended a football game at Stratton High School one evening. All of the children from East Park were walking home together as a group. Uncle Cecil would not walk with the other youth, but took them another way home. He told them "you don't need to be talking to those boys." In another story, Mother said she once met a man that Uncle Cecil had worked with for many years. When he learned that she was his sister, the man was shocked. He said that Uncle Cecil never mentioned that he had sisters.

After Aunt Lettie been dead for one year, Uncle Cecil remarried. We felt the only reason he remarried was because he needed someone to cook and wash his clothes. He could not boil water and felt a woman's place was in the kitchen. Both of his wives, however, still worked outside the home.

Uncle Cecil was not a favorite uncle either. Once as a child the family was sitting on the front porch talking; I was sitting on the steps. Something was said and I made a comment. Uncle Cecil snapped at me telling me, "Children were made to be seen not heard, so shut up

Miss Fassy." I never forgot that incident. My feelings were hurt. Even after I was married, when my husband and I visited Uncle Cecil, he would have the conversation mainly with my husband, as if I were not present in the room. When our father left and it was determined that he was not returning, Uncle Cecil brought Mother a 100 lb. sack of flour. Mother said that was all he ever gave us.

Aunt Mary and her husband Willie Johnson also had a brick house built when I was about thirteen years old. When they got married Aunt Mary owned a house that was purchased by her first husband, Uncle John Florence, who died as a result of a mining accident. It was a two room house. After she married Uncle Willie, they had three rooms added to the house. They would later build a brick house across the street. They lived on the same street as Uncle Cecil.

Aunt Mary was not my favorite aunt, even though she and Mother were only two years apart in age. She was always grumpy and complaining. When we went to her house to watch television, she made us feel very uncomfortable. She was full of "don'ts." We would have to "sit up straight" on the sofa; "don't ruffle the rugs," "don't talk" while watching television. We would often tell Mother that we did not want to go to Aunt Mary's house to watch television. Mother would say that they had asked us to come. We would tell her that we were glad that God made her our mother and not Aunt Mary. At Christmas Aunt Mary and Uncle Willie would have lots of presents under the tree for us. They were things that we needed for school such as socks, underwear, coats, and sweaters.

Before Uncle Willie married Aunt Mary, he had a reputation of being a person with street smarts (gangster or thug). He hung out at juke joints and went for "bad." He was known to carry a gun (pistol) and once cut a man with a knife. He was a short stocky man with a big head and a thick neck. He had a big flat nose and big thick lips. After marrying Aunt Mary, he turned his life around. He joined the church, and became an usher. I guess you would say, "He got religion." He was not my favorite uncle either. They had no children.

It was not until I was a grown woman talking to my sisters that we learned he had sexually molested all three of us during our teen years. He would ask Mother if I could come over there and pick the turned-in hair-bumps on his face. Aunt Mary was at work on Saturday operating the elevator at J.C. Penney Department store. I would beg Mother not to go, but she would insist. He would beg me not to tell Mother. He was always finding ways to buy us nice things. He paid for my formal gown for the debutante cotillion ball. I hated him for what he did. But, neither I nor my sisters ever told Mother what he did.

Aunt Mary was four years older than Uncle Willie. She was very suspicious of him and thought that he was seeing other women. She was especially suspicious of him giving women rides in their 1955 Chevrolet. She would look in the car hunting for hairpins or any evidence of a woman being in the car. Little did she know that the women were her own nieces?

She was also mean to Uncle Willie. She once told us that she threw a newly baked pound cake down the basement stairs. Uncle Willie liked warm pound cake with butter. She said, "He is just greedy and cannot wait for the cake to cool." That was one of the meanest things I had ever heard. She did other mean things to him as well. Mother said she would withhold sex from him as punishment.

Uncle Willie died at the age of 42 from lung cancer. He was a coal miner for 20 years. He was a motorman, which was a higher paying job than a coal loader. He was also a heavy smoker as was Aunt Mary. He smoked Phillip Morris cigarettes. It was not a filtered cigarette. The exposure to coal dust and the cigarette smoke probably had a significant impact on his demise.

Aunt Catherine and Uncle George were renters living in a coal-camp called Winding Gulf. Their house was located just across the railroad tracks. During the summers I was allowed to spend the weekend with Aunt Catherine and Uncle George. They lived on the hillside across the street from the railroad tracks. I would watch the train cars back up to the tipple and see coal coming down the shoot into the cars. Imagine the polluted air that the families were breathing every day. They later moved to another section of Winding Gulf away from the railroad track. I remember attending their little white church that sat on a hillside. Aunt Catherine was Uncle George's second wife.

His first wife died and left him with two young children: Jimmy, seven, and Isaiah (Pig), five years old. Aunt Catherine was 22 years old, Uncle George was 32. They were both at least 10 years older than me.

To get to Winding Gulf, the roads were very narrow and winding. The town was located deep inside a group of mountains. That is how the town got its name, I am certain. There was a company store owned by the owners of the coal mines. I recall going there and seeing a "potbelly" stove sitting in the center of the store. Aunt Catherine and Uncle George eventually left Winding Gulf and moved to East Park, in the same community where we lived, where they bought a house.

Uncle George was a big man. He stood about six feet two inches. He had big bones and had a bald head and a large pointed nose. He was very comical. He reminded me of Red Fox, the comedian. He was always telling jokes. He would tell us ghost stories of when he was a boy and dead people would come back to life. We loved to hear his stories and he enjoyed telling them. Aunt Catherine was also a fun lady. She had a bad habit of embellishing the truth. She was somewhat of a "drama queen" but we loved her more than any other aunt.

Both Uncle Cecil and Aunt Lettie and Uncle Willie and Aunt Mary were financially sound and could have afforded to send me to college. They never offered and I never asked. Aunt Lettie sent me ten dollars a month while I was in nursing school. That is all the financial support I received from any of them.

Uncle Brandon was Mother's oldest brother. He was named for his father, Thomas (Tom), but used his middle name. He was married twice. Ironically, both of his wives were named Annie Mae. One was Lewis the other Morris. To Ms. Morris was born five children. We called her Aunt Annie Mae. She was twelve years younger than Uncle Brandon.

He had a major drinking problem. He was an alcoholic. When he got drunk he would come to our house and tell Mother that we was going to kill Aunt Annie Mae. Mother would scold him, telling him it was his liquor talking, that he should stop drinking, and that he was not going to kill anybody. He would often fight Aunt Annie Mae. She was a strong and stocky woman who often won the fights. He did eventually kill her. He was drinking and they got into a fight. He stabbed her in the chest with a butcher knife. She was 38 years old. Two of his older children saw it happen. He went to prison for murder. He died in 1978 a lonesome man sitting in a rented room.

Aunt Leila was another favorite aunt. She was my father's older sister. She and Uncle Dewey lived in Fayette County, West Virginia, in a small community called Harlem Heights near the city of Oak Hill, WV. Before moving there, they had lived in Montgomery, WV. Uncle Dewey was also a coal miner. I spent summers with them during my teen years. Aunt Leila was a diabetic. She gave herself insulin. It was not until I became a nurse that I realized Aunt Leila was not eating properly as a diabetic. She was overweight and never exercised. Her exercise was sitting on the front porch. She appeared to love Uncle Dewey very much. They had pet names for each other, Buddy. On Sundays, she would lay out his clothes for him to wear to church. This included his suit, shirt, tie, underwear, and shoes and socks. They eventually moved to Charlottesville, Virginia, where she died from complications due to diabetes in 1976. Uncle Dewey wandered off from the trailer where they lived one day and disappeared. His body was never found. We often thought that he went in the woods where Aunt Leila was buried looking for her grave. The authorities searched the woods but never found his body.

Some of my aunts worked as domestics except for Aunt Mary, who was the elevator operator at the J.C. Penney department store. I don't recall Aunt Leila working. The domestics usually worked for young white professional families. I was often recommended to be a babysitter for their children. One of the families that I sat for was Dr. Robert and Mrs. Patricia Hyatt. Mrs. Hyatt had trained as a nurse but never worked as one. They often asked me what I wanted to do after I finished high school. Of course, I told them that I wanted to become a nurse.

Mrs. Hyatt, was a member of an organization called the Beckley Women's Axillary, whose membership consisted of physician's wives. She was instrumental in getting me a three year scholarship from the organization to go to nursing school. I believe I was the first black student to be awarded this scholarship. They would move to

Rochester, Minnesota, where Dr. Hyatt was a cardiac specialist at the Mayo Clinic. They would eventually divorce and Mrs. Hyatt married a childhood sweetheart. She died several years ago. Their son Mark became a psychiatrist and daughter Mindy became a Ph.D. psychologist. I spoke to Dr. Hyatt and the two children several years ago. Dr. Hyatt was in his eighties and still working.

I was accepted into the nursing program at St. Margaret's Hospital School of Nursing in Charleston, West Virginia. A pre-entrance examination was required. Mrs. Hyatt drove me to Charleston to take the examination, took me out to lunch afterwards, and drove me back home. I passed the examination. However, St. Margaret's closed and I was transferred to St. Mary's Hospital School of Nursing in Clarksburg, West Virginia. Both institutions were operated under the Order of the Sisters of St. Joseph. Charleston, West Virginia, was 86 miles from Beckley; Clarksburg, West Virginia, was 136 miles. My only option for nursing school was through a hospital since none of the local colleges offered a nursing program. I would have had to go out of state and that would have cost more money.

Beckley had one college; Beckley College, established in 1933. It was a two year junior college until 1991. It did not have a nursing department. The name was changed to The College of West Virginia in 1991. In 2001 the name was again changed to Mountain State University. The institution was known to be military friendly for veterans coming from the service. It prepared them for the workforce. The school lost its accreditation in 2012 after its president was fired. The university closed in 2013. In March 2015, the property was sold to West Virginia University.

There were three colleges established for African Americans in West Virginia. First Storer College was established in 1867 in Harpers Ferry, West Virginia. Storer College was co-educational and interracial. It was on the grounds of Storer College that the Niagara Movement had its initial formation in 1909. One of the founding members was W.E.B. Dubois. The Niagara Movement was the precursor of the National Association for the Advancement of Colored People (NAACP). Storer College closed June 1955. (Anthony, 1867-1891)

31

Then West Virginia Colored Institute was established in 1891 under the second Morrill Act. The Act provided for land-grant institutions for black students. It was the only all African American college in West Virginia at that time. The land had previously been a slave plantation. Governor William H. Cabell of Virginia had a son, Samuel I. Cabell. Samuel had children by a slave, Mary Barnes. He was never allowed to marry Barnes because of her slave status. He moved Mary and her children to Kanawha County, West Virginia, and purchased property. In his will, he left all of his property to Mary Barnes and her children, which was the property upon which West Virginia Colored Institute was established. Mary donated the property to the state. The name of the school was later changed to West Virginia Institute and West Virginia State College. My mother attended this college in 1937-1939. She did not graduate but instead eloped with my father to Giles County, Virginia, to get married in June 1940. (Haught, 1971)

Lastly, in 1895 Bluefield Colored Institute was established in Mercer County, West Virginia. It served as a training school for Negro teachers. In 1931 the school was renamed Bluefield State Teacher's College and in 1943 to Bluefield State College. My sister Margaret attended Bluefield State College for one year before joining the Army. African American students protested in 2015 because the college was being transformed into a technical college and the increased enrollment was white commuter students who were overwhelming the African American students. (Wikipedia, Bluefield State College, 2017) (Meraji, 2013)

Prior to graduating from Stratton High School, I had a boyfriend, Rodney Coleman. He was one year ahead of me. We dated during my junior and senior years. He wanted to get married. He was a fat, sloppy boy, however, he was a great cook. He took the commercial class in food management in the vocational side of school. The class prepared meals for students. He once made me a fruitcake. My goal in life was not to get married and raise a family, but to have a professional career initially and family later. After he graduated, he and his family moved to New York. I went off to nursing school the following year. I saw him some 30 years later at a high school reunion. He was slimmer and cleaner- cut. He had worked for the automobile industry in Detroit, Michigan, for over 30 years and was retired. He would later move to California where his children were living. He told me that he had two children, a son and a daughter; the same as me and my husband. He was divorced from his wife. I learned last year (2015) that he died.

CHAPTER 3

COAL MINER'S VERSUS SHARE CROPPERS

My father and all of my uncles were coal miners. My maternal grandfather, who was born in Russell County, Virginia, moved to McDowell County West Virginia, to work in the coal mines. His father, Jarrett L. Smith, was a farmer. It appears according to the U.S. census data in 1900, 1910, and 1920, all of my grandfather's siblings were either coal miners, worked on the railroad, worked with coke ovens, or worked in the steel mills of West Virginia, Pennsylvania, and Ohio. All of the men in my life during my growing up in West Virginia were coal miners.

Booker T. Washington[3] and Carter G. Woodson, both African American icons, had a time in their young lives when they too worked in the coal mines of West Virginia. Booker T. Washington was a young boy when he worked in both the coal mines and salt mines in Kanawha County, West Virginia. Many young children were exploited by being made to work in the coal mines. Booker T. Washington would eventually become a Sunday School Teacher and the church clerk at the African Zion Baptist Church in Malden, McDowell County, West Virginia, in 1880, and the year my grandfather was born. (Harlan, 1971)

Carter G. Woodson[4] was born in Buckingham, Virginia. His family moved to Huntington, West Virginia, where they learned there

---

[3] Booker T. Washington was the founder of Tuskegee Institute (Tuskegee University) Tuskegee, AL.

[4] Carter G. Woodson established Black History Week in February 1926.

was being built a high school for blacks. Woodson moved to Fayette County where he worked in the coal mines. He would later return to Fayette County to teach school after completing high school in Huntington. (Bickley, 2006)

Both Booker T. Washington and Carter G. Woodson's coal mining experiences were brief. They were fortunate enough to get out early and to get an education so that they had no need to ever return to the life of coal mining.

I never considered the importance of unions until I studied for my Master's Degree in Public Health at the Johns Hopkins School of Public Health. There is where I actually learned the impact that John L. Lewis had on the coal mining industry. He was instrumental in organizing and unionizing the coal mine workers. I recall hearing my uncles talk about John L. Lewis but did not understand who he was and what the significance of his name meant. He called for the first major coal union strike in 1919. Working conditions were hazardous to the health of workers and the wages were poor. Under his leadership the first Federal Mine Safety Act was passed by Congress in 1952. (AFL-CIO, 2017)

There were many injuries associated with working in coal mines. When I was in elementary school one of my classmates, Sam Wiley's, father was killed in the mines. Our families were related by marriage. That was a frightening time. Mr. Wiley's sister lived next door. We lived in a small, very close-knit community where everyone knew everyone. So when there was a tragedy, the entire community felt the pain. Both my father and my Uncle George suffered injuries due to mining accidents. Uncle Willie died from lung cancer. Not only did he work in the coal mines, breathing cold dust for years, but he also smoked cigarettes. During those days men were not required to wear respirators. Doing genealogy research, I learned that in 1910 my maternal grandfather's brother, Clark Smith, was killed when a coal trolley cut off both of his legs. He left behind four children and a pregnant wife.

Coal mine owners were quick to allege that the accidents occurring in the mines were caused by carelessness, neglect, or ignorance of the workers. When really the owners were lax in providing safe working conditions and training. African American men were placed in the most dangerous places and the most hazardous conditions. "Coal mines were often filled with odorless and tasteless methane gas. Canary birds that were easily stressed and sensitive to toxic gases such as carbon monoxide and methane, were used up until the 1980s." (Shepard, 2007).

One of the worst mining explosions in the history of the United States occurred in Fairmont, West Virginia, on December 6, 1907. Three hundred sixty-one (361) men were killed in the Monongahela #6 & #8 coal mines. (Monongah Mine Diaster, January 1908) On November 6, 1923, there was a mine explosion in Beckley, West Virginia's Glen Rogers's mine, where 23 men were killed.

Coal mining was the occupation of most African American men and poor white men in West Virginia, especially southern West Virginia. Russel County, Virginia, where my maternal grandfather was born, lies in the southern most county of Virginia just a few miles from the Kentucky and Tennessee borders. Granddaddy moved to Wise County in 1910 to work in the coal mines. He lived in a coal-camp called Toms Creek. The coal camp housed Italians, Hungarians, Polish, Slavish, Russians, Australians, Negroes, and poor whites. The coal company produced coal, coke, and iron. The housing was segregated according to race and ethnicity. The Negro housing was segregated from the other groups. There were "Talley Town" that housed the Italians, "Hunk Town" that housed the Hungarians, "Pink Town" that housed the poor whites and "Big Bug Row" that housed the supervisors, superintendents, and managers of the coal mines. The section called "Hardaway Row" was where the foreman for the coal mines lived. None of the houses had running water. Only the whites, Italians, Hungarians, and other white immigrants were allowed to attend the school. Their building contained six rooms and a full size basement, steam heat, and a large auditorium that would seat 300 people. There was a company store that had three rooms in the rear where the Negro children were allowed to attend school. The Company Store provided a butcher shop, dry goods department, grocery department, and a furniture store. Other items that could be purchased included cigarettes, candy, ice cream, and sodas. (Perry)

What is the rationale in living in segregated housing when all of these poor people, no matter the nationality, worked side by side in those dirty, hazardous coal mines, took the same risk from the exposures of the coal dust and dangerous gases and looked out for each other? All took the same risk. The Superintendents and other managers did not live in the same neighborhood as the other poor whites. What does that tell you? In addition, the coal mines had a monopoly on the miners. The miners lived in the mine-owned houses, bought from the mine-owned store, and worked in the mines. The mine owners owned the workers. They were treated no differently than the sharecroppers in the Deep South. Remember the song by Tennessee Ernie Ford, *"I Owe my Soul to the Company Store"?* (Fishback, Dec. 1986)

"The Southern West Virginia coal fields comprised five districts known as New River, Pocahontas, Kanawha, Logan, and Mingo. The chief producing counties were McDowell, Logan, Raleigh, Fayette, Kanawha, Mingo, Mercer, Boone, Wyoming, Greenbrier, and Clay. The average number of persons employed in the five southern coal districts in 1928 was 77,000." (The Hospital Contract System in the Southern West Virginia Coal Fields, page 165).

The Coal Company also owned the hospital for miners. Anyone employed in the mines, whether they lived in Toms Creek or not, as long as they worked in the coal mines, could be seen. There was also a "company doctor" who made house calls for a fee of $2.00. This fee was taken out of the men's paycheck. Even if the condition was a work-related injury, the miner had to pay for it from his paycheck. (Williams, 1932)

(In May 2013 my daughter and I visited Wise County Virginia searching for history of my ancestors to be included in the family tree. We observed a lot of coal trucks and tipples where there was active coal mining. The area is still very rural. It must not have looked much different in 1910 when my grandfather lived there).

All of my mother's brothers were diagnosed with "Black Lung Disease" (Pneumonocosis). Most were coal loaders, which was one of the most hazardous positons in the mines. They were the employees who crawled on their knees or lay on their stomachs using a pick to break up the coal from the earth or coal vein as it was called. Once the coal was loosened, it had to be shoveled and thrown into trolley cars and pulled out of the mines. Uncle Willie became a motorman. The salary of a motorman in 1950 was $74.70 a week or $14.94 a day. This positon paid more and few blacks held it. The Motorman operated motors which were used in the transportation of loaded cars by switches or sidings in mines to the shaft and empty cars from the shaft to the switches of sidings. Loaded and empty cars were hauled to and from the switches by mules. During the early days, young boys led the mules. (I.W.W, 1922)

After being discharged from the Army in 1948, and until he deserted the family, my father worked in the mines. When he came home the main things he did were work in the coal mines, read western novels, and drink liquor. His drinking became worse over time. He would often not come home for several days at a time. When he did come home he was drunk and fought Mother. As a coal miner Daddy was able to cut script before payday. Script was the coal miner's credit card. (Wilson, 2006) They were coin shaped and could only be spent in the company store where the coal mines were located. The coins were valued at 80 to 85 cents on the dollar. This script was charged against the miners payroll account and deducted from his next payday. By the time the fees for medical services were taken out and in some cases rent was deducted from the payroll account, nothing was left to draw come payday. That was the case of my father. Once I recall Mother crying on Daddy's payday. She said that Daddy only brought home $11.00. There was nothing to pay bills or purchase food. Fortunately, we did not have to pay rent. He had cut script to purchase liquor. Once some of his friends brought him home. He was covered in mud from his head to his toes. He had fallen into a mud hole. I had to help Mother undress him. The next morning Daddy did not even recall how he had gotten home.

My father sustained a fractured hand in a mining accident. Uncle John Florence, Aunt Mary's first husband, had a serious mining accident that caused him to be bedridden. I was too young to know what the injury was. I imagined it was a back injury. Uncle George, however, had the most serious mining accident causing him to be hospitalized for his injuries. He walked with a limp for the rest of his life. He died from a heart attack in 1983 at age of 79 years old. He had been diagnosed with Black Lung Disease.

An article written in 2013 by The Center for Public Integrity titled, "Breathless and Burdened," focused on retired coal miners who were denied Black Lung (pneumoconiosis) health benefits from the coal companies where they had worked and been exposed to coal dust for many years without the benefit of respirators. The author, Chris Hamby, found that both attorneys and physicians representing the coal companies withheld information pertinent to the claims and misread chest x-rays. One of those was a renowned radiologist on the staff of Johns Hopkins Hospital in Baltimore, Maryland. Even after other radiologists saw signs of Black Lung disease on the x-rays, the judge on the case dismissed their report in favor of the Johns Hopkins report which indicated the x-rays were normal. Several coal miners have filed lawsuits against the companies for which they worked and were denied claims.

During the 1920s and 1930s there were at least 18 hospitals located in Southern West Virginia. The miners had $1.50 to $2.00 deducted from their payroll before they were paid. These funds were paid to the hospital that the coal mining companies had made a contract with to provide health care services to its employees and their family members. These funds also covered medical care for work-related injuries. In essence, the coal miner was required to pay for his own injuries sustained in the line of duty. The coal mine companies eventually hired law firms to scrutinize the claims of its employees who filed claims of injury from pneumoconiosis. It was not until 1969 that the Federal Government passed legislation mandating that owners of Coal Companies control the amount of coal dust in mines. The Black Lung Benefit Act (BLBA) was not legislated until 1995. (The Black Lung Benefits Act provided monthly benefits and medical benefits to coal miners totally disabled from Pneumoconiosis arising from employment in or around the nation's coal mines. The Act also provided monthly benefits to the miner's dependent survivors if Pneumoconiosis caused or hastened the miner's death. The Division of Coal Mine Worker's Compensation (DCMWC) within the U.S. Department of Labor Employment Standards Administration's Office of Worker's Compensation Program (OWCP) adjudicates and processes claims filed by coal miners and their survivors under the BLBA). [Information from the U.S. Department of Labor website].

The book, *Miners and Medicine: West Virginia Memories,* written by Dr. Claude A. Frazier provides great information about the injuries, workplace occupational exposures to coal dust, and the medical treatment of coal miners. It describes the early days of medicine when physicians first became aware of the health impact of coal mining. The one thing that his book did not emphasize was the fact that all African American coal miners were given the most dangerous and hazardous assignments. Those included coal loaders and coke pullers.

PART TWO

DEVELOPING INTO A NURSE

The history of nursing goes back to Florence Nightingale (1854). The history of blacks in nursing goes back to slavery. It was the African American bonded women that had to take care of sick slaves and at times family members of the slave owners. Many were midwives, delivering babies for the enslaved as well as the slave owner's female relatives. Nursing certainly was not considered a profession. One of these women was Harriett Tubman. Some of these women were gifted and did a magnificent job offering nursing care for relatives and neighbors during reconstruction. So, actually, African American women were nursing long before Florence Nightingale was born. (Covey, 1989)

Once nursing schools were established in the United States, African American women were not allowed to attend. The black physicians and some white philanthropists were instrumental in establishing black hospitals. Nursing schools became an essential component of these institutions. Nursing was considered a trade not a profession. There was the thinking that women were born nurses, i.e., they were born with the instinct to nurse. This stereotyping of women had a detrimental effect on the profession. It was in 1879 that the first black nurse graduated from an established nursing school. She was Mary Mahoney (Hine, Black Women in White: Racial Conflict and Cooperation in the Nursing Profession 1890-1950, 1989). Very few white schools accepted African American students. The few that did admit them had a limit on how many they would accept. Most of the training was from nursing schools affiliated with black hospitals.

Eventually, schools such as Tuskegee Institute (University) in Alabama and Dillard University in New Orleans, Louisiana, would establish some of the first baccalaureate programs for African American nurses. The nurses gained some clinical experience from the John A. Andrew Hospital in Tuskegee, Alabama, but were sent out of state up north for other clinical skills training. Tuskegee also had a program for midwifery during my stay there from 1968-1972. (Hine, Black Women in White: Racial Conflict and Cooperation in the Nursing Profession 1890-1950, 1989)

In West Virginia, there were no African American nursing programs affiliated with the two black colleges; West Virginia State and Bluefield State. Most of the nursing schools were affiliated with a hospital. My life's goal was to become a nurse. I wanted to help the sick and especially black sick individuals. So I went to a hospital school of nursing for my nursing education. Notice I said education not training.

CHAPTER 4

ST. MARY'S

I entered St. Mary's Hospital School of Nursing in August 1959 at the age of eighteen. My roommate was from Fairmont, West Virginia. Betty and I were the only two African American students in a class of 30. All other students were white. Most of the students were Catholic and were from Clarksburg and surrounding communities. Betty was Methodist; I was Baptist.

The initial three months students were considered to be on probation. After that time, if you were not showing potential, you were sent home. Betty and I made a pact that we were not going to be sent home. We felt we needed each other's support. It worked. We became close friends and we both graduated.

St. Mary's Hospital School of Nursing was affiliated with the Catholic Church. It was run by the Order of the Sisters of St. Joseph. The school of nursing was established in 1909 when the Harrison County Hospital's operation and management was taken over by the Sisters of St. Joseph, Wheeling, West Virginia. The school operated for sixty-seven years before it closed in 1976 and merged with Union Protestant Hospital. The nursing school was transferred to Salem College, in Salem, West Virginia. The college would later develop an alliance with Tokyo University, Tokyo, Japan, changing its name to Salem International University. The nursing program is similar to the one that I attended at Bowie State College (now University). It provides opportunity for nurses with Associate Degrees and diplomas in nursing to obtain a Bachelor's Degree in Nursing. Salem International University offers an Associate Degree in Nursing and a Vocational Nursing Program (vocational practical nurse, VPN).

In 1959, St. Mary's Hospital School of Nursing offered a three year program. Because I lived 136 miles, an eight hour trip on the Greyhound bus, I could not go home often. So my weekends were spent on campus. There were some other students who lived a distance and could not go home every weekend. There were other students in the Medical Laboratory program from Louisiana and Mississippi who were on campus. Most of these students were African American and Catholic. We often spent leisure time together. One of those students was Mary Ellen Smith. On one occasion the two of us participated in a sit-in at one of the restaurants in Clarksburg. We went in together and as soon as we sat down someone turned out the lights. There were several individuals sitting at the counter and several sitting in booths. One of the employees walked over to us and told us that we could not be served because the restaurant was closed. I said if they were closed why were their customers sitting in the dark eating? Then we were told that I could not eat there. Mary Ellen could stay. At that point we both got up and left. During my senior year, I was permitted to work in the hospital every other weekend for $8.00 per day.

All student nurses were required to attend chapel every morning before going to the hospital wards. It did not matter if you were not Catholic. We were not required to say their prayers or the Rosary; only our own prayers. I never had the urge to change my denomination from Baptist to Catholic. I always had a problem with the students going to "confession." I thought it was a mockery. I had a discussion with some of the black Catholic girls several times. My question was, how do you continue go to confession with no intention of changing your ways? They prayed for the same sins every week. That did not make sense to me. If you were sorry for your sin, then you would not do it again and again.

The student uniform consisted of a white uniform that was stiff with starch and measured 13 inches from the floor. To be in uniform meant all nurses had to wear their cap, have a black and red ball point pen, and a pair of bandage scissors in their uniform pocket. The school washed the uniforms, we had to wash our personal clothing items. Today, nurses no longer wear caps and the uniforms are more like 36 inches from the floor or pants are worn.

St. Mary's was a Catholic hospital and the wards were not segregated according to race. As a student nurse, it never occurred to me whether patients had insurance. Paying their bills was not a concern. We were concerned about learning what ailments the patients suffered and how to treat them.

On one occasion, the issue of "Socialized Medicine" came up in the political arena. Two of the physicians, Dr. Gilman and Dr. Rose, asked the nurses to go to the polls and vote against this issue. They were convinced that Socialized Medicine was being introduced into the American medical system. Too bad they are dead and did not see the passage of the Affordable Health Care Act. I often wonder how they felt when Medicaid and Medicare became law.

We had one month off from classes during the summer; one month per year. Most classes were taught by nurses. The physicians were considered guest lecturers. Mrs. Kathleen McGann taught Nursing Arts; Miss Wilma Pertz taught Pharmacology; Mrs. Mazzi taught Obstetrics and Gynecology; Mrs. Virginia Waugh and Mrs. Brummage taught Medical & Surgical Nursing; Mrs. Thornton, the hospital dietician taught Nutrition and Dietetics; and Ms. Aman was the Clinical Supervisor in the Operating Room who taught Infection Control. The librarian taught English Composition and Public Speaking. Sister Laurentia was the Pediatric instructor. Mrs. Kirkpatrick, a professor from West Virginia University, drove down from Morgantown to teach Anatomy and Physiology. We had labs where we were required to dissect cats that had been preserved in formaldehyde. We learned the insertion of muscles and tendons. There was a male professor who also came from West Virginia University to teach Chemistry. We were all required to spend one week at the Harrison County Health Department and three months in Pittsburgh, Pennsylvania at St. Francis Hospital for psychiatric nursing.

Student living in the dormitory was a typical experience. We had a kitchenette located on each floor. Each floor separated the students according to classification. The freshman were on the top floor. The juniors were on the floor below and the seniors were on the floor below the juniors. The nuns lived above the freshman. The kitchenette had a stove and refrigerator, table and chairs. The refrigerator was stocked weekly with fresh loaves of sliced bread, milk, a large jar of peanut butter, and a large jar of jelly. When studying late at night, the gathering place was in the kitchenette where peanut butter and jelly sandwiches were flying. I ate so many that I swore to myself, when I got a job and started working I was not going to eat any peanut butter and jelly sandwiches. To this day, I still do not like them. I ate enough to last me for the rest of my life.

I was fortunate to have an aunt who would send me $10 every month for spending change. That was Aunt Lettie, Uncle Cecil's wife. That was a lot of money in 1960. I used it to purchase my personal supplies such as toiletries and other items. There was a laundry room on each floor. There were slide-in dryers that pulled out from the wall. Once the clothes were washed, the dryer rods were pulled and the clothes hung on each rod. The rods were pushed back into the wall where heat was present to dry the clothes. It took about 3 hours for the clothes to dry. Then they had to be ironed. They were so stiff and hard that they had to be sprinkled with water prior to being ironed. That was how many of my Saturdays were spent.

During the time that I studied at St. Mary's Hospital, we used glass intravenous bottles with plastic tubing. Needles were reused after being sharpened and sterilized in the Central Supply Department. The bottles were discarded. This is where all instruments and equipment were sterilized. The surgical trays were prepared here. A nurse was in charge of this department

Nurses at St. Mary's Hospital were not treated with respect or as professionals. I could never understand why. When a physician entered the nurses' station, all nurses had to stand up and give up their seats. That made no sense to me. The nurses' charting was just as important as the physician's orders. It was as if what the nurses were doing was not important. However, after an era of litigation, it became clear that nursing notes were vital information. If they were not documented, it did not happen.

There was one nun, Sister Margaret Theresa, who never got out of her seat when the physicians entered the nursing station. She was a huge woman. She was grossly obese and could have easily weighed 400 pounds. A lot of nurses were afraid of her. When she walked down the hallway there was a big wave of white habit flowing in the wind. There was one particular physician that she went with for his rounds. You can imagine what the students had to say about that once we got back in the dormitory. We believed she was sweet on the doctor. That was a ha! ha! moment for us.

Another disrespectful encounter that nurses experienced in the operating room was with one particular physician. When he finished the surgical procedure, he would remove his gloves and pop the scrub nurse in the buttock. Today, that would be considered sexual harassment.

There were many sad and exciting cases. While working as a student in the hospital three stands out the most; one was a white teenage girl who came into the hospital in labor. She was admitted to the Obstetrics and Gynecology ward. She told the doctor that she had a stomach ache from eating green apples. She said that she did not know she was pregnant. The infant was born without a brain. Its body was in a frog-like position. The condition is called "anencephaly". The baby's brain did not develop. The baby was living but died shortly thereafter. The doctor would not let the mother see it. That was frightening since I had seen only one other baby being born.

The second case was a white woman who was admitted for a prolapsed uterus. It was actually suspended outside her vagina and she was holding it up by wearing a sanitary napkin. Apparently, it had been outside so long that the tissue at the end of her cervix had eroded and had become ulcerated. I don't recall if she had cancer, but it was frightening for a student nurse to encounter such a sight.

And yet on another occasion, I was working on the male ward. One of the patients had what is called a hydrocele (water in the scrotal sac). It was absolutely the biggest scrotum that I had seen in my whole life. I have never seen another like it. I don't know how the man was able to walk. It was almost as large as a grapefruit. The condition is called "elephantiasis" which means gross enlargement of a body part. In this case it was the scrotum. The scrotum is frequently affected. (Staff, Diseases and Conditions: Hydrocele, 2014)

Why these individuals neglected to seek medical treatment is one question that has lingered with me all these many years. Did they have health insurance? Did they not have money? Were they afraid of having surgery? Were they afraid of a feared diagnosis? There are so many questions and reasons. But Clarksburg was a poor town and even though the majority of the population was white, they were poor whites.

CHAPTER 5

CLARKSBURG, HOME OF STONEWALL JACKSON

Clarksburg, Harrison County, West Virginia is located in the northern part of the state. It is noted for being the home of Thomas J. "Stonewall" Jackson. Clarksburg is the county seat for Harrison County. It did not have the coal mine reputation of Southern West Virginia. The African American population was 3%, the other 97% was white. That is just a microcosm of the State of West Virginia. (Haymond, 1910)

I graduated from St. Mary's Hospital School of Nursing in 1962. My first job was as a staff nurse in the Pediatrics Department of the hospital. Working with children was one of the services that I enjoyed the most. I found a one-bedroom apartment on First Street and shared it with a roommate, Eleanor Henderson, who had been in the class above me in nursing school. Eleanor's home was in Clarksburg, even though she grew up in Fairmont. We both worked rotating shifts, so we rarely saw each other. Eleanor's mother gave us a set of twin beds. Aunt Catherine gave us dishes, silverware, and table cloths. Dr. Moats, a dentist and our landlord, gave us an overstuffed arm chair. We went to a second-hand store and together purchased a gas range, sofa and love seat, and a kitchen table with four chairs. I purchased a television stand and Eleanor purchased a television. We lived together for one year. When I left, the only thing I took was the TV stand that I had purchased. I paid Eleanor for what we had purchased together. I had purchased a mini electric washing machine. It was a small wringer machine that would hold two bed sheets at a time. I sold the machine before leaving Clarksburg.

It was a sunny day and I was hanging clothes on the clothesline across the street in Eleanor's grandmother's back yard. One of the neighbors yelled out of the window at me. "Go in the house and turn the TV on!" she exclaimed, screaming. I said, "What happened?" She answered, "THE PRESIDENT HAS BEEN SHOT!" My heart began pounding immediately. I could barely run across the street. I turned the television on to see the immediate coverage of President Kennedy's death being reported. I could not believe my ears or my eyes. Yet, I was seeing and hearing just as events were happening. What was the world coming to? How could this happen? What next? Of course for the next several days our eyes were glued to the television watching the funeral and the hunt for the killer. My heart went out to Jackie Kennedy and those little children.

I met my first serious boyfriend in Clarksburg. He was the son of my hairdresser. Gene (Eugene Donaldson) was a student at Purdue University while I was living in Clarksburg. He had won a football scholarship to attend Purdue. He graduated from Kelly Miller High School where he was an outstanding athlete and a popular football player. He was six feet two inches tall and had a stocky build. He had very dark skinned and a large flat nose. I thought he was 'tall, dark, and handsome.' He was very active on campus. He joined the Omega Psi Phi fraternity and was the Vice Basilar at the time I visited the university during one of the homecoming celebrations. While he was busy with his basilar duties, he did not want his best friend to dance with me. I asked him why. He said, "I don't want any other man putting his hands on you." We dated for three years. The year he graduated he gave me a friendship cultured pearl ring. His family was sure that we were going to get married. We discussed it but never became formally engaged. One reason for my reluctance was that he was too jealous! It was abnormal. He would get upset if another man looked at me.

In addition, his brother was married and treated his wife like a piece of property. She was a prisoner in her own home. She could not go shopping unless her husband took her. It became so bad that she

54

actually left him. Her mother and stepfather lived in Pennsylvania. One morning after her husband left for work, her mother and stepfather had a rental truck waiting down the street. They packed her and the three children and moved them to Pennsylvania. They moved everything out of the house except the kitchen table and one bed. When Gene's brother came home from work he found his wife and three children gone. I knew that I did not want to be in such a situation.

Gene's mother told me that her husband was extremely jealous of her also. She once told me that she had worked late in the beauty shop one evening. As she was walking home, she felt someone behind her. She became frightened. As she approached her house the person identified himself. It was her husband. She said she believed that he was outside her place of employment watching her to make sure she was telling the truth about working late. Gene's mother and I became great friends and maintained a lifelong relationship. She died two weeks before my mother died in July 2009.

I developed a very close relationship with Gene's family. His aunts were very kind to me. They had developed a sense that I was going to be part of their family, even though Gene and I were not engaged. His aunt, Myrtle, was a very dear friend. She had two sons, Andrew and Michael. I would often stay at her home on the weekends, sharing her son's bedroom. They were like little brothers to me. We had some great times together. I am sure they were disappointed when the relationship between their cousin and I dissolved. I have become friends with Andrew on Facebook.

The pay at St. Mary's Hospital was awful. I could not see myself living in this slow moving community with such a low paying job for the rest of my life. In 2010 the population in Harrison County was 16,578. The median household income from 2009-2013 was $35,201. (In 2001 my salary was over $60,000). I was offered a job as a RN staff nurse at George Washington Hospital in Washington, D.C in 1964. (Resouces, 2000 to 2012)

After moving to Washington, the relationship with Gene cooled. He was drafted by the Washington Redskins but was cut early. Our last date was in Washington, D.C. He was later drafted by a team in

Canada and played football there for several years. I lost contact with him and did not hear from him again until his mother celebrated her 80th birthday in 1998. His Aunt Myrtle invited me to attend. My husband went with me. Gene looked much different than I had remembered. His hair was black but he sported a thick white beard. He had gained weight. I imagined he weighed close to 300 pounds. He looked like a wild man but he was very cordial to me and my husband. His mother sent me a brown envelope in 2002. It contained Gene's obituary. He had died of a heart attack at the age of 60 years old. He had been married and had two children. He had obtained a Master's Degree in Human Resource Management and had served in the Army in Vietnam as a 2nd Lt. I spoke to his mother on several occasions afterwards. In July 2009, I called and could not reach her. I called her son, Sonny, who told me that he had buried his mother the day before I called.

PART THREE

INTRODUCTION TO WASHINGTON D.C.

When I moved to Washington, D.C., I thought that I was moving north. Of course, it was north of West Virginia, but it was below the Mason-Dixon Line. There was just as much prejudice and discrimination here as in West Virginia. The amazing thing that I noticed immediately was the number of African Americans living in the District of Columbia. To see black men as bus drivers was something that I had not seen in West Virginia. Everywhere I looked I saw black people. That was quite different in West Virginia where Blacks constituted only 3% of the population.

CHAPTER 6

MISS BIGELOW/SURROGATE MOTHER

I moved to Washington, D.C. ,in the spring of 1964. My landlady was Ms. Alice Bigelow. She had been referred to me by Dr. Moats who was my landlord in Clarksburg, West Virginia. She and his wife had been classmates at Kelly Miller High School in Clarksburg. Ms. Bigelow lived in a large two-story, three bedroom house in upper northwest which she had purchased for her father who had died several years before I arrived. She lived alone but found joy in renting her bedrooms to young women. The previous boarder had been a young lady from Jamaica who was a dental student at Howard University School of Dentistry. At the time I moved in Miss Bigelow was working for the Federal Government at the General Accounting Office. She had never been married. We got along well from the very beginning. I lived with Ms. Bigelow for one year. I needed to be able to learn the city before I branched out on my own.

Ms. Bigelow was a member of Metropolitan African Methodist Episcopal Church in Washington D.C. Baptist was the denomination that I had grown up in. I had attended Shiloh Baptist Church since I had previously met Rev. Henry Gregory Jr. who was on the ministerial staff of the church. I met him through his father, Rev. Henry Gregory Sr., who was the pastor of Water Street Baptist Church where I attended in Clarksburg, West Virginia. Rev. Henry Gregory Jr. came to Clarksburg to attend his sister's wedding. All of the young people of the church were invited. Rev. Gregory made several visits to

Clarksburg to see me following his sister's wedding, but nothing came of it. We just remained friends.

After moving to Washington, D.C., Rev. Gregory introduced me to his best friend, Pennington Greene. He was a school teacher and drove a taxi part-time. We dated several times. After being intimate with him, I became pregnant. Here I was, new to Washington, D.C., in a new job, and pregnant. I knew I could not have a baby now and ruin my career and my life. Pennington found a woman who performed illegal abortions. I went to her home, paid her $75 and had an abortion. Yes, I had an illegal abortion just like so many women in the 60s, before *Roe vs Wade*. That was cathartic! If the courts overturn *Roe vs Wade*, women who want abortions will go back to "back- alley" abortions. I knew two girls that attended high school with me who died from illegal abortions. Fortunately for me, God saved my life. I told Rev. Gregory what had happened and what I had gone through. He had prayer with me but we never discussed it again. That was the end of my relationship with Pennington Greene, who told me that he was separated from his wife and was paying child support for his two children in Baltimore. This is why he needed to drive a taxi. I wanted nothing to do with this situation. The relationship dissolved at this point. I would eventually see him several years later on two separate occasions after I was married; once on the bus and once at a local hotel where the Kappa's Ball was held. I learned that he died in 2008 at the age of seventy-three.

Ms. Bigelow asked me to attend Metropolitan African Methodist Episcopal Church with her one Sunday and I agreed to do so. The pastor was Rev. G. Dewey Robinson. Since I worked rotating shift at George Washington University Hospital, and only got one weekend off during the month, I told her that the next time I had a weekend off I would go to church with her. The next weekend that I was off was in the month of January 1965. It snowed the entire week and the temperatures were below zero. The roads had been scraped and salt put down but the sidewalks were still snowy, icy, and slippery. On Saturday night, Ms. Bigelow asked if I were still going to church with her on Sunday. I told her, "If you go, I am going." So on Sunday morning we climbed up the hill to 14th Street to catch the D.C. Transit bus. I knew nothing about the African Methodist Episcopal denomination. I did not recall hearing anything about its founder, Richard Allen. Most churches in West Virginia were Baptist.

That Sunday following services, Ms. Bigelow, who was a stewardess, had a meeting. She suggested that I could wait for her, catch the bus, or catch a cab to go home. She introduced me to one of the young associate ministers, Rev. Edgar James. Rev. James stated that he could take me home. He was driving a taxi as a part-time job. I agreed to let him drive me home. He brought along a friend, Willie Oxendine. Willie told me that he had just come back from the Great Lakes following a Navy assignment and that he had graduated from Tuskegee Institute. I was impressed with him and when he smiled he sported a gold tooth. However, the next time I saw him he did not have the gold tooth. I was surprised. The gold had been only temporary. Two weeks after meeting him we went on our first date to the Bohemian Caverns on U Street, N.W to see Cannonball Adderley.

Willie (Bill) help me to move during the spring of 1965 from Ms. Bigelow's house into my own apartment on New Hampshire Avenue ,which was one block from George Washington University Hospital, enabling me to walk to work. During the month of May, Bill invited me to attend the Penn Relays in Philadelphia, Pennsylvania. After we returned to Washington, D.C., that evening he asked me to marry him. I accepted the proposal because I was smitten by this gentleman.

Miss Bigelow became a life-long friend. When I told her that I was going to marry Willie, she was very pleased. She told me that she thought he came from a very fine family since she knew his sister, Magoline Ramsey and her husband, Damon, who was a trustee of the church.

Ms. Bigelow had only one sister who had died many years earlier. Her sister married but never had any children. She would eventually adopt a girl child. She told me that after her sister died, she brought the adopted daughter to Washington to live with her. The girl was so unruly and disobedient that she had to send her back home to live with her father. Her name was Adrienne. She would eventually marry and join her husband's faith as a Muslim. They had five children. Adrienne would leave her husband and children and move to Canada where she married a white man old enough to be her father.

When we moved to Tuskegee, Alabama, I kept in touch Ms. Bigelow. While we were there in 1969 she married Mr. Charles L. Curry, a member of Metropolitan AME Church. He was 72 and she was 58 years old. This was her first marriage and his third. When we moved back to Maryland we met Mr. Curry. It was a long time before I could remember to call her Mrs. Curry. Mr. Curry was a likable person. It seemed like I had known him as long as Mrs. Curry. He had retired from working as a porter on the railroad. He once told me that he had served Al Capone in the train car where he worked. He divorced his first wife with whom he had two daughters. His second wife, Rosetta Dodson, died in 1957. His oldest daughter, Anna, died of cancer at an early age. His daughter Mary lived in California and worked for Los Angeles County Government. She retired on disability after having brain surgery.

Mary Curry was diagnosed with a brain tumor. Following the surgery she had a stroke. She had been married twice but had no children. She had divorced both husbands. She was placed in a nursing care facility following the stroke. The only contact that Mr. and Mrs. Curry had with her was through a co-worker named Maurice Govan. He would call Mrs. Curry and give a status update on Mary's condition.

Mrs. Curry died in 1989. Mr. Curry had been admitted to a nursing care facility prior to her death. Mr. Govan continued to keep the lines of communication open for Mary. Before Mrs. Curry died, she asked me and my husband that in the event anything were to happen to her would be look after Mr. Curry? We agreed that we would, never knowing where this promise would lead.

When Mrs. Curry died her adopted niece, Adrienne, came down from Canada. She had her husband with her. I was anticipating that she came so she could plan her aunt's funeral. I was mistaken. She came to see how much money Mrs. Curry left her. I had to take time off work in order to plan Mrs. Curry's funeral. I had never buried anyone and did not know the first thing about planning a funeral. I relied on my husband's oldest sister, Magoline, to guide me. I approached the president of the Stewardess Board but that was like striking a brick wall. I was spoken to so ugly. It was awful! After that encounter, I never had anything to say to this lady except to acknowledge her presence.

I would become the permanent conservative for Mr. Curry. He was in a Manor Care facility in Hyattsville, Maryland. As soon as Medicaid learned of Mrs. Curry's death, the State of Maryland immediately cut off his nursing home benefits. After the nursing home facility management learned that Medicaid had cut off his benefits they immediately raised Mr. Curry's monthly fee and did so monthly. They told me that he was worth $185,000 dollars. Apparently, they had planned to get every penny. That was before the property had been appraised. I immediately began looking for another facility to move him into. I was able to get him admitted into the Villa Rosa Nursing Home located less than a mile from my home. The facility was operated by the Catholic Church and took only individuals who could pay. It did not accept Medicaid or Medicare. Their rates were half of what the Manor Care had been charging him when he left.

Mr. Curry loved Metropolitan AME Church. He was very knowledgeable about the denomination because he had been a life -long AME member. It was a joy learning from him. He had memorized where each Bishop had been assigned. While he was in the nursing home one of the members of Metropolitan ordered the Christian Recorder for him. He enjoyed hearing me reading it to him from cover to cover.

Mr. Curry was a WWI veteran. He died in 1992 at the age of 97 years old. Prior to his death, I had to go to California to check on the status of his daughter, Mary. She was still in a nursing home there. One day I called the nursing home to let Mr. Curry speak to his daughter. I was told that she was no longer there and had been moved by her son. I was alarmed, because Mary had no children! What I learned was her former co-worker, Maurice Govan, who was posing as her "play son," had moved her. He had stopped paying her nursing home fees and was four months behind. I told Mr. Curry what I had learned. He asked me if I would go out to California and see what was going on with his daughter. I had to get emergency temporary guardianship. I located an attorney, Gary Cooper, through the Legal Aid Society of California. I flew out to California with my sister-in-law, Magoline Ramsey. We found that Maurice Govan, who had worked with Mary Curry for Los Angeles County Government, had moved Mary into the residence of a woman with children who was on welfare. Mr. Govan was paying this woman $100 a week to take care of Mary.

I went to the bank and closed her account. I found that Mr. Govan had been forging Mary's signature to cash checks. I then went to the personnel office for Los Angeles County retirees and had them to send checks direct deposit to the new account that I had opened with $25 of my own money. Then I went to the Social Security Administration and had them stop sending checks to the old account and send them to the new one.

We flew back to Maryland and I contacted the Nursing Home where she had resided. I spoke to the administrator and told her that Mr. Govan was a fraud and an impostor. Mary Curry had no children. Mr. Govan was a former co-worker. I asked the administrator if they would take Mary back into the facility. She agreed that they would hold a bed for her. The social worker set up transportation for an ambulance to pick her up. I contacted the attorney and flew back to California on the "red-eye" and met the attorney at the court house. I hired a taxi at the airport for the day to take me to court and to the nursing home. I met attorney Gary Cooper at the courthouse. The Probate Judge gave me permanent authority as a foreign conservator to take care of Mary Curry's affairs. I called the nursing home and alerted the social worker that she could call the ambulance to have Mary transferred back to the nursing home. I had the taxi to drive me to the nursing home. I arrived there just minutes after the ambulance had delivered her back to the facility. The nursing home staff told me that Mary was smiling and that they felt she remembered them and appeared to be happy. The nursing home administrator ask me not to file charges against Mr. Govan because they did not want him arrested. They wanted to file charges against him and garnish his check to recoup their money. I told her that I had no intentions of filing any charges against Mr. Govan. I was Mary Curry's conservator for 19 years until she died in July 2009. Mr. Charles L. Curry, her father, died in 1992 at the age of 97 years old. The monies that I acquired from her father, Charles Curry, covered the expenses for me throughout the years. I flew out to Los Angeles, California, several times and would go to the nursing facility unannounced. I always found Mary in good condition. She was clean and well- groomed as was her room. The facility was bright and sunny and without odors.

My husband filed taxes for Mary Curry. We learned that she had not filed any taxes since she retired, which had been some seven years earlier. The only thing that Mr. Govan did for her was steal her few pennies that she was getting from her retirement check and SSI. He had been forging her name to her checking account. The SSI was direct deposit and the retirement checks were going to his home. He did away with all of Mary's furniture and personal possessions. We never found out what he did with them but surmised that he sold them. I never heard anything more from Mr. Govan. I have learned that he still lives in Los Angeles and is 74 years old at this writing. So in the end, I was responsible for burying Mrs. Curry, Mr. Curry, and his daughter, Mary. I made arrangements with a funeral home so that in the event of Mary's death, they had authority to collect the body and cremate her. I prepaid for everything. When she died, everything went very smoothly. I did not have to make another trip to California. When I received the phone call from the nursing home in California that Mary had died, I was taking care of my mother in West Virginia who was in her last two weeks of life .Mary died two weeks before my mother died.

How many elderly citizens who have no living relatives are mistreated by unscrupulous individuals? According to the National Center on Elder Abuse, "Perpetrators are most likely to be adult children or spouses, more likely to be male, to have history of past or current substance abuse, to have mental or physical health problems, to have history of trouble with the police, to be socially isolated, to be unemployed or have financial problems, and to be experiencing major stress." (Hall & Crosby, 2016) I don't know how many categories applied to Mr. Govan. He was posing as Mary Curry's "play son." He was employed by Los Angeles County government. I would assume he had financial problems or else he was just greedy and took advantage of her because he surmised that since Mrs. Curry was dead and Mr. Curry was in the nursing home, he had free access to her and her property.

In 2002, I was recognized and honored by the Washington Tuskegee Alumni Association for Humanitarian service for assisting Mary Curry.

CHAPTER 7

ENGAGEMENT AND MARRIAGE

After I moved into my own apartment in May, Bill Oxendine took me to Philadelphia to see the Penn Relays. That evening he proposed to me. Ms. Bigelow was very happy for me and insisted on buying my bridal veil. She also went shopping with me to purchase my wedding gown.

Willie Lee "Bill" Oxendine was born in Sumter, South Carolina, to Mary Oxendine. His mother was not married when he was born. She married when her children were older. Bill's father's name was Telford "Buddy" Curry. Bill said that his father never acknowledged him as his son even though the resemblance was significant. His father called himself a preacher. What kind of individual called himself called by God to spread the word of God, yet does not acknowledge a child that he has fathered? Bill was an outstanding student in high school and graduated from college (Tuskegee Institute). His mother had 10 children, all with a different father. Bill's family was poor as was mine. He was living with his oldest sister, Magoline, when we met. He later told me that it was this sister that helped finance his education at Tuskegee. He also shared with me the ancestry of his last name. Oxendine is a Native American name. The name Oxendine came from the Lumbee Indian nation. While living, Magoline started the family tree. She was able to find their great grandmother. I pursued this link and found her mother and father. Her father was an Oxendine and her mother was a Benehaley who was also of Lumbee heritage. There are many Oxendines in North and South Carolina.

We were married on September 4, 1965, in Beckley, West Virginia. It was a beautiful sunny but windy day. Bill's family traveled from Washington, D.C., to attend the wedding. His sister Ruth was one of my bridesmaids. When we returned to Washington, D.C., following the wedding, I became ill with a high fever and sore throat. I was seen and treated in the George Washington University Hospital emergency room. I was placed on antibiotics. That delayed our wedding trip to New York by four days. We returned from West Virginia to Washington on Sunday night. I was seen in the hospital on Monday morning and we did not leave for New York until Friday. The honeymoon was short. We lived in my apartment for one year. Then we moved to an apartment in upper northwest near Walter Reed Army Medical Center. We lived in Washington our first three years of marriage. I worked at George Washington Hospital and Bill worked at Goddard Space Flight Center in Greenbelt, Maryland, as an Electronic Technician.

When I began working at George Washington Hospital, the first thing I noticed was there were a number of African American staff nurses and physicians. The nurses did not have to get up and give the physician their seats. The nurses were actually respected for their work. One of my first assignments was working in a ten-bed ward on a medical unit. That was a killer. The ward contained all females. When you went into the room it was like you had entered a lion's den. To answer the request of one patient, you would have to do something for every one of the other female patients before leaving the room. None of the nurses wanted to be assigned to that room. The hospital eventually did away with the large wards such as this, finding that those types of wards were breeding grounds for infections.

There were three patients that I will never forget in that ten bed ward. One was a white female age 28 who died of cirrhosis of the liver from alcoholism. I learn to perform abdominal paracentesis on her. I could not imagine a person so young dying from alcoholism.

The second was a huge (grossly obese) black female who was so large that it took three nurses to give her a bath. Two nurses held up the abdominal fat pad while the third nurse did the washing. She needed a blood transfusion. Her religion, Jehovah's Witness, did not believe in blood transfusions. It became a legal matter and was settled in court. She eventually died.

The third was a white female who was crippled with rheumatoid arthritis. She had the most deformities of any individual I have ever seen with that form of arthritis. But she had the sweetest disposition in spite of her suffering. She developed bedsores because she was so bony, even with the constant turning and even getting her up in the chair. At that time sugar was used to pack the wounds of bed sores (pressure wounds). I don't know if that procedure is used anymore. During this time patients stayed in the hospital for weeks and even months at a time. Patients were admitted for "tests'. Now these tests are performed on an outpatient basis. There was one patient who actually lived on the unit. That was her home. Apparently, when I arrived she had been living there for several years. Of course she was wealthy. Today she would have been sent to a nursing home.

I was required to rotate shifts. One week I would be on evening (3 P.M.- 11 P.M.). The next week I would be assigned to night shift (11 P.M. to 7 A.M.). I was seldom scheduled for the day shift (7 A.M.- 3 P.M.). I may be off at least one weekend a month. After one year, I could not take any more of this shift rotation. I had difficulty sleeping. My body could not get adjusted to what time I was getting up or what time I was going to bed. Also, my new husband was working at Goddard Space Flight Center or (NASA) in Greenbelt, Maryland, and he was on a rotating shift also. We seldom got to see each other. However, he was off every weekend. I began looking for a job outside the hospital.

The first position I found was working at Howard University on a research project with a physician, Dr. Vernon Straughn. The project enrolled obese women. They were placed on an appetite suppressant and a special diet. They were required to report to the clinic weekly for blood pressure and weight - monitoring. Many of these women did not have any health insurance and came to the clinic for medical problems as well as weight management. All services were free. I later worked for the Columbia Lighthouse for the Blind, teaching first aid to blind clients. It was while I was working at this facility that we had our first child, a son, Terry. I left the Columbia Lighthouse when we moved to Alabama. I would later accept a positon at a Health Maintenance Organization, Group Health Association. I also worked in Occupational Health, both in the hospital and in private industry which occupied the majority of my nursing career until I went back to school.

Our son was five (5) months old when we heard the news on the television that Martin Luther King had been shot. My husband and I discussed the event, without much surprise. We felt that something like this would happen to him. He was too popular and had too much power to be a black man. We knew that some white person would find a way to shut him up.

The day after Martin Luther King was shot, I had planned to go downtown Washington to do some shopping. There were three elderly Jewish ladies who lived across the hall from us and babysat for me on occasion. So on this day they kept our son for me. I walked one block to 14th Street and caught the bus. After arriving downtown something did not feel right. I noticed black boys and men running in and out of stores with items of clothing and televisions and other items in their hands. The bus driver said that he thought that there was going to be a riot. My heart began to pound. I got off the bus and crossed the street to catch the next bus going back home even though it took me two hours to get home. The police had begun blocking off streets. I went home and turned on the television to see a full blown riot taking place. I could not believe what I was seeing.

While my husband was working at Goddard, they were performing experiments, testing the coating of satellites to determine how much heat and friction it could tolerate. As an electronic technician he was limited in his scope of practice. He felt that he wanted to become an engineer so he could be more involved in the experiments. He began taking classes at George Washington University on a part-time basis. We decided if he really wanted to become an engineer he needed to go back to school full time. Going back to Tuskegee, Alabama, where he had received his first college degree; where living expenses were much cheaper, and where we could afford for him to attend school full time seemed like the best option. He applied to Tuskegee Institute and was accepted into their Electrical Engineering program. He would earn his bachelor's degree in Electrical Engineering in 1971 the same year our daughter was born at John A. Andrew Hospital.

After graduating, Bill had applied for a job with the Federal Power Commission (Federal Energy Regulatory Commission) located in Washington, D.C.. However, we left Alabama moving to Drexel Hill, Pennsylvania, where Bill accepted a job working with the U.S. Naval Engineering Center located in Philadelphia, Pennsylvania. I was a stay at-home mom. While there I became pregnant again and miscarried. We lived there for one year. He was contacted by the personnel office of the Federal Power Commission one year later and offered a job. We had wanted to return to that area after he graduated so he accepted the positon. The Navy department allowed him to move since he would be working for the Federal Government.

We moved to Maryland, initially living in an apartment while we looked for a house. We bought our first home in Riverdale, Maryland, where we lived for five years. We moved to Mitchellville, Maryland, in 1978 because we had outgrown the house in Riverdale. We have spent the majority of our married life in this location where we celebrated 50 years of marriage in 2015.

CHAPTER 8

ALABAMA ROUND

Bill was accepted into the Electrical Engineering Program at Tuskegee Institute (University) his alma mater in 1968. Our son Terry was six months old. Never did I think I would ever be living in the State of Alabama. I had heard so many negative things (horror stories) about the state as I was growing up. It was located in the Deep South and steaming with segregation and discrimination. African Americans had been lynched there. The KKK burned crosses on the lawns of African Americans. It was not any place that I wanted to be. During the years of my nursing school experience, the country was encountering the civil rights movement; the "sit-ins" and the "freedom riders." Alabama was in the headlines almost on a weekly basis.

While in high school, I had watched on television George Wallace, the governor of Alabama, standing in the doorway of a school to prevent integration. His infamous comment "segregation today, segregation tomorrow, segregation forever," were words that I never forgot. I find it ironic that I lived to see George Wallace taken down. After being shot by an insane gunman while running for the office of President of the United States, in the State of Maryland where I lived, he had plenty of time to remember his past and how he got to where he was. Sitting in that wheelchair for years, God brought him down to the point that he actually repented for what he had done and said. In the 1980s he actually apologized for some of the ugly comments that he made against black people.

Also, while in high school I saw on television Governor Orval Faubus of Arkansas use the National Guard to block the entrance of the building to prevent nine black children from integrating the high school. I heard my mother talk about the Montgomery, Alabama, bus boycott. So I had no yearning to go any further south than West Virginia, where I was born.

Prior to moving to Alabama we had contacted a woman who was referred to us by one of my husband's classmates. She identified a gentleman who had a house for rent. Mr. Jackson's house sat at the intersection of two busy streets. When we arrived we walked through the house and found all of the walls in the house had been painted kelly green. He had rented the house to students previously. The stove had not been cleaned in a year. We spent the first week cleaning and painting the house before we could move in with our infant son. As soon as we were able to find another house, we moved where it was safer to raise our son.

I applied for a job at the Veteran Administration Hospital prior to leaving Washington, D.C., and was offered a position. When I went to the VA Hospital I learned that they had placed a freeze on all hiring. I was disappointed that I had not been notified of the change. However, there was a hospital on the Tuskegee Institute's campus called the John A. Andrew Hospital. I went to the hospital to see if they had any openings for a registered nurse. The Director of Nursing, Mrs. Claudia Stallworth, asked when I could start. There was a vacancy in the Emergency Room. She wanted me to start the following day. I told her that I had not found a babysitter for our six month old son. She was more than willing to help us find a babysitter, which she did promptly. One of the nurses working at the hospital knew a woman who took care of children. Fortunately for us, she lived two houses down the street from us.

The Veteran Administration Hospital had a very interesting history. It was established in 1921 following World War II when African American soldiers coming home had no place to receive health care due to segregation and racial discrimination. With the aggressive action of the National Association for the Advancement of Colored

People (NAACP), the National Medical Association (made up of black physicians), and Dr. Robert R. Moton, president of Tuskegee Institute; Dr. Moton allowed the Federal Government to build a veteran's hospital on three hundred acres of land owned by Tuskegee Institute. The facility cost $2.5 million and consisted of 600 beds in 27 permanent buildings.

The VA Hospital was completed in 1923. The first superintendent was a white physician. His plan was to open the hospital with a full staff of white physicians and nurses to care for an all-black population. Dr. Moton wrote President Harding asking that black physicians and nurses be hired and allowed to take care of the black veterans. The request was granted. (Morais, 1967)

With this move, the Ku Klux Klan was incensed that black men would have hospital services for neuropsychiatric and tubercular health. It never ceases to amaze me that the white man doesn't want black citizens who have served this country to receive healthcare services in their own hospital, but yet it would be okay for white nurses to serve black men. The issue was that the services being offered to these black men were not available to them because they decided that they would not be in a facility with black men. That was their choice.

It is ironic that in today's times some whites and the Republican Party, in particular, still hold the same beliefs. A good example is their trying to dismantle the Affordable Health Care Act. Not only do poor African Americans benefit but also poor whites, Latinos, and any other race of people who have been without health insurance for generations.

Well I missed the opportunity to work in this historic institution. Instead, I went to work at the John A. Andrew Hospital on the campus of then Tuskegee Institute (now Tuskegee University). It had its own history. John A. Andrew Hospital was originally the Tuskegee Institute Hospital and Nurse Training School established in 1892. It serviced students and faculty. In 1900 it was expanded to include 25 beds and was opened to the community. In 1913 Tuskegee Institute received a financial donation from Mrs. Elizabeth Mason of Boston, Massachusetts, the granddaughter of the Honorable John Albion Andrew, the 25th Governor of Massachusetts, for whom the hospital was named. The hospital expanded in 1929, 1940, and 1946. When I arrived at the hospital in 1968 it contained 175 beds. (Wikipedia, John Albion Andrew, 2015) (Eugene Dibble & Louis A Rabb, 1961)

Alabama is the nation's seventh poorest state. It has ranked as one of the poorest states in the United States since the Civil War. The long history of slavery, Jim Crow laws, segregation, and racial discrimination has had a significant impact on the health of African Americans and has held them in poverty. Because of discrimination and Jim Crow laws, African Americans were denied access to health care services in the state. The opening of John A. Andrew Hospital to the community was a blessing to the poor blacks living in Alabama. (Placeholder1) (Project, 2013)

There were other hospitals in the state that were established specifically to care for African Americans. One such facility was the City of St. Jude, owned and established by the Roman Catholic Church in Montgomery, Alabama. The hospital was founded by an ordained priest, Father Harold Purcell. He was so shocked at the plight of the health of African Americans in Alabama in 1934 that he was granted funds and 56 acres of land by Bishop Tolen. The hospital was dedicated in 1938. St Jude Hospital was nationally recognized when it aided those civil rights participants during the March from Selma to Montgomery in 1965. John A. Andrew Hospital was ahead of its time in serving the black community. (Wikipedia, City of St. Jude, 2015)

Before I discuss some of the shocking experiences that I observed in the Emergency Room (ER), I must discuss my encounter with Mohammed Ali. He, apparently, made a visit to Tuskegee's campus during the time he was resisting going in the military to serve in Vietnam. He experienced some trauma while handling a rifle. The butt of the gun hit him in the lip or jaw. All of a sudden I heard a great commotion in the hallway that leads to the ER. There was Mr. Ali with his entourage. He came in and I began to access his injury. His comment to me was, "Why aren't you asking me for my autograph?" I told him I was on duty and was there to treat his injury. He countered back by saying, "I'll break those little bony legs." That was not funny to me and did not make me want his autograph. I had never found boxers as role models. Anyone who will stand up in a ring and get his or her head boxed is not someone that I would look up to. Even though he considered himself a champion, to me he was a loser. Look what happened to him in the end. I do not call him a champion to this day. He is a loser in a worse way. He has developed a neurological disorder that is a result of having his head bashed constantly.

I was not prepared for what I would see coming through the doors of the Emergency Room at the hospital. There were many pediatric cases. The children were very sick and most had to be admitted to the Pediatric ward. There were several memorable cases but the one that affected me the most was a mother who came in with the infant wrapped in a filthy baby blanket. The mother laid the infant on the examination table and opened the blanket. The infant was not moving or making any kind of sounds. The infant was suffering from severe malnutrition. There before my eyes was the signs of a starving infant. His body was skin and bones. The skin was so loose it was suspended from the bones of its ribcage. Its abdomen was grossly distended and its eyes were sunken into the back of the head. I was speechless. I almost could not get my breath. What was I seeing in the United States of America, the richest country in the world in 1968? A starving infant. I called the pediatrician, Dr. Campbell, and asked if he would come immediately to the ER that I had an infant that looked like it was suffering from severe malnutrition. He came immediately and admitted the infant to the hospital. What is so sad about this starving infant is the fact that today, in the 21st century, children are still starving.

I never forgot the condition of that child. Years later I was working in a building in Maryland where an abortion clinic was housed on the upper level. On a daily basis, I would see young white men and women, some with babies in strollers, picketing the clinic. I would imagine that mother in Alabama would not have had the baby if she had a choice of abortion.

I spoke to one of the protesters one day and asked them if they would be willing to adopt an infant if the mother decided to have the baby and wanted to give it away because she could not care for it. The individual just looked at me with a hollow expression. Would they have been willing to provide food to the mother in Alabama to save that infant's life? It's okay to be against abortions. If you don't want to have an abortion then don't have one, but don't try to force your beliefs on others. They have a choice to act on their beliefs. This is America.

The incidents of women arriving to the ER having delivered their babies on the way to the hospital were enormous. Many had traveled hundreds of miles, passing white hospitals, only to deliver before arriving at John A. Andrew. Dr. Henry Foster, the Obstetrics and Gynecologist at the hospital, received a grant from the Department of Health and Human Services. The grant provided for free prenatal care that could be obtained in community centers throughout Macon County, Alabama, and free health care services for delivery. Many women knew of this opportunity. The grant also offered preventive health services to women and children. These poor women had no health insurance and Medicaid had not been made available before this time.

In addition to the plight of poverty, there was a lot of folk medicine practiced in Alabama. I believe it was much more than I learned growing up in West Virginia. On one occasion, a young man was brought into the ER by his family with a white powdery substance noted in the top of his head. My first impression was that the ceiling or something had fallen and hit him on the top of his head. I was badly mistaken. The parents told me that the white substance was Epson Salt. They said that he had been "acting out" and they had put the Epson Salt on top of his head to control the demons. I don't know how long the young man had been exhibiting these symptoms, but I would surmise that they had waited until they could no longer control his behavior. He was seen and it was determined that he had some mental health condition. He was sent to a hospital in Montgomery, Alabama.

In another case, a teenager was brought in by his family with a grossly swollen foot that was obviously infected. Taking a history, we learned that he had sustained burns when he ran into a burning house to save his little sister. His family had been putting "ink" on the foot to "draw out the fire." The teenager was in severe pain. He too was sent to a hospital in Montgomery. I prayed that the young person would not lose his foot.

When I arrived at Tuskegee, the Medicare and Medicaid Bills had been signed into law by President Johnson in 1965 but had not been implemented in the state of Alabama. During the time that I was there, both were implemented. There was an immediate noticeable impact on the number of uninsured patients that were coming to the hospital. Once patients qualified for both Medicare (the elderly) and/or Medicaid (the poor), the white physicians began to see black patients. There was definitely a drop in the number of patients traveling long distances. These blacks went to the white physicians even though they had to sit in segregated waiting rooms and received substandard and inferior care.

Unfortunately, I had an occasion to experience such discrimination in a South Carolina white physician's office in 1967. My husband's home was located in Sumter, South Carolina. We were there for a Christmas holiday visit when I became ill with a sore throat and a high fever. We went to the emergency room at the Toomey Hospital located in town. We were referred to a private physician's office with an appointment scheduled for the following morning.

When we arrived at the white physician's office, we were directed away from the waiting room where plush sofas and arm chairs were in place for seating white patients. The room was in the back of that waiting room with two wooden benches for the black patients to sit. This was the first time in my life that I had encountered stark overt segregation in a health care setting as a nurse.

When I was taken into the examination room, I noticed that the physician had obtained his degree from George Washington University Medical School. I told the physician that my son was born at George Washington University Hospital and that my first job as a registered nurse in Washington, D.C., was at the same hospital where he had received his medical degree. He turned several shades of red. It was obvious that he was embarrassed. He apologized for the waiting room. He tried to explain that things were different in South Carolina. To soften the blow, he gave me a discount on the bill. I never went back to see him or any other physician in South Carolina. When we passed the black physician's office, we noticed a line of patients standing all the way around the building. The waiting room was full and patients who were standing outside. He was the only African American physician in Sumter. The blacks were willing to stand in long lines rather that experience the Jim Crow services of white physicians.

After working in the Emergency Room at John A. Andrew for one year, the Director of Nursing reassigned me. This was done without any consultation with me. She told me that Dean Lillian Harvey, who was the Dean of the School of Nursing at Tuskegee Institute and also over the nursing department at the hospital, ordered the transfer. She had been pleased with what I had accomplished in the ER, establishing an OB/GYN emergency delivery tray, emergency EYE tray, and organizing the medications and instruments for easy access. She was also aware that I had previous pediatric experience before coming to the hospital. So, after returning from vacation, I learned that I was the Head Nurse of the Pediatric Department.

The registered nurse whom I replaced, was a Tuskegee graduate. Dean Harvey was not pleased with her service. She was transferred to the Emergency Room. She would later leave the hospital and become the last nurse that worked on the "Tuskegee Syphilis Study."

I continued to see poverty at its worse. Children were admitted that had illnesses and injuries because of their poor living conditions. There were several cases that stood out. An infant that was admitted with bed sores. The infant (3 months old), apparently, was left to lay in wet diapers for hours at a time. The ammonia in the urine burned the child's skin and the tissue had broken down. The infant was treated and sent home. Dr. Campbell was reluctant to let the infant go home but he decided not to report the mother. He gave her a stiff reprimand. He told the mother if the child was seen again he would report her to Child Protective Services.

We did see the same infant again several months later. She had grown some and was taking her first steps, or so I thought she should have been. When she was admitted to the Pediatric ward, her thigh was swollen and very tender. The child refused to stand up. Dr.

Campbell ordered an x-ray of her thigh which showed a fracture of the femur.

Dr. Campbell referred the child to the Orthopedist, Dr. John Hume, who placed her in a cast. Dr. Campbell called the mother and requested that she come to the hospital. When she arrived, he asked her what happened to the child's leg. She reported that the child had fallen off the bed. He wanted to know how high the bed was. She described a normal bed. Dr. Campbell called Child Protective Services and reported child neglect. The child was placed in foster care. As soon as the pain was relieved and the extremity was stabilized, the child immediately stood up in bed and began walking around the rails.

In another case, there was a two year old child that was admitted with severe burns to his head, neck, and face, caused by a pan of hot grits that he pulled from the stove. He was a patient for a very long time and became a family member of the nursing staff. Everyone knew him. Dougie was a joy. When he was ready to be discharged from the hospital he had outgrown his clothes. I bought him an outfit to wear home. The staff donated toys for him and I agreed to deliver them to his home. When I went to his home, I was shocked seeing the living condition in which this child was being raised. There was a big hole in the flooring allowing you to see the earth underneath the floor in the main living area. The floor was made of rough boards that had never been sanded. There was a stack of children's clothing in one corner of the room from the floor to the ceiling. There was minimal furniture in the room. That was the front or main entrance room to the house. I did not go further. I dropped off the toys and left. The home was unsafe, unclean, and unsanitary. I was happy and thankful that the toddler's wounds were completely healed when he went home.

What was most alarming was learning after leaving Tuskegee that the Syphilis Study of which the U.S. Public Health Service perpetrated on black men in Tuskegee was still going on during our stay there. I never heard a word spoken about the study the entire three years that I lived there. I learned that Mrs. Kennibrew, the RN that I replaced in the Pediatric Department at John A. Andrew Hospital, would become the second and final nurse supporting the project, by reading the book, *Bad Blood: The Tuskegee Syphilis Experiment,* by James H. Jones. The study ended in 1972 a year after we left Tuskegee. We were there from August 1968 to May 1971. It is unimaginable that such horror was going on in the community and no one knew, especially the physicians at the hospital or the nurses in the community. Of course, other than *Bad Blood,* many other books have been written about the experiments on these innocent black men that were going on for over 40 years. Treatment for syphilis was withheld from them when penicillin was discovered to be a cure. The white doctors wanted to see what the disease did to the body without treatment. Again, black men were treated like experimental animals (they could have just as easily been a study of rats). (Jones, 1981) Today many African Americans do not have much faith in medical treatment received from white physicians. This is especially true in the south by uneducated African Americans. Some can still tell horror stories that they have experienced. And I am certain that all are true. There are many other cases where African Americans have been used as experimental animals. (Washington, 2006)

One of those famous cases was that of case of Henrietta Lacks. Cells from her cervix were taken without her permission. The Johns Hopkins Hospital staff learned that her cells would not die outside her body. They took the cells and began selling them. The cells became a multimillion dollar industry of which her children knew nothing. It was some 20 years later when a reporter started asking questions that her family learned what had happened to their mother's cells. They had received not one penny from the selling of their mother's tissue. (Skloot, 2010) There have been other cases much worse. During slavery, African American women were used a guinea pigs to test procedures for the repair of Vesico-vaginal Fistulas which were tears between the vagina and rectum, a complication of childbirth. Dr. J. Marion Sims performed multiply procedures on these women. The women had to be held down by several individuals while these experimental procedures were performed over and over. One patient had 30 procedures performed on her. This monster, Dr. Sims, earned the title of being the Father of Gynecology and has a statue standing in Central Park in New York City. Other horror stories can be found by reading the book, (Washington, 2006).

There was a time when African Americans did not want to be treated by black doctors because they felt they did not have the training that the white doctors had. Most of these doctors were educated at the two most prestigious black colleges in the land, Howard University and Meharry Medical School. Some physicians were even educated at integrated colleges and trained at white or integrated hospitals. The blacks had been brainwashed. Even though white doctors had segregated waiting rooms and did not give the blacks the same treatment as whites they preferred medical treatment from white physicians. How unfortunate! Over time, blacks have overcome this stigma. (Thomas J. Ward, 2003)

I recently read an article in the *Huffington Post* written by Jessica Cumberbatch-Anderson, entitled "Racial Bias among Doctors Linked to Dissatisfaction with Care." She referenced an article published by the March issue of the *American Journal of Public Health*, where researchers found that two-thirds of doctors harbored "unconscious" racial biases toward patients of color. In a study done by Dr. Lisa A. Cooper, MD, M.P.H. at Johns Hopkins University; she found that white physicians tended to order fewer test and perform fewer procedures on African Americans than whites when treating the same diseases and there was no difference in the ability to pay.

I was in disbelief after reading Dr. Henry Foster's book, *Making a Difference*, that when he was selected as a candidate for the position of Surgeon General of the United States by then President Bill Clinton, one of the congressmen who was interviewing him accused him of knowing about the Syphilis Study and doing nothing about it. (Henry W Foster, 1997). Did he expect black physicians to halt a project sponsored by the U.S. Public Health Service operated by white physicians? That was a shameful accusation and an insult. The senator or congressman who made that accusation did not deserve to be reelected. He or she was a disgrace to their office and a mean-spirited individual. There is no question he/she was a Republican. That's how they think. They are known for being evil-spirited when it comes to blacks. Dr. Foster would have been an outstanding Surgeon General. I wonder if Dr. Foster had been a white physician would the comments have been different. After all, the physicians working for the Public Health Department were all white. I don't believe any one of them served any time in prison. Politics is one of the ugliest forms of activities of government in the United States. We are going to other countries to show them the way to democracy? That is truly a joke! I often wonder if politicians have a conscience. They lie, then stand before the camera and declare that they are Christians. I wonder what God they serve; especially the Evangelicals.

While I was in Tuskegee, Alabama, working at the John A. Andrew Hospital, I became pregnant with our second child. Dr. Foster provided my prenatal care. However, when I went into labor, he was out of town and a physician from Georgia who was covering for him delivered our daughter. Mary was born with a birth defect. Her right hand did not develop properly leaving her with two missing fingers. She only had a thumb, index, and middle fingers which were webbed together. As any mother would be, I was distraught when I saw my child. I had taken such good care of myself, keeping my appointments, taking my pre-natal vitamins, eating properly. But what I did not know was taking the drug Bendectin for nausea during the early pregnancy would have a negative impact on my child. I would learn many years later that it had side effects which interfered with the development of fetal limbs. That is another story to write.

During my career at John A. Andrew Hospital, I had the opportunity to get acquainted with all of the physicians on staff. They were as follows:

Dr. Thomas M. Campbell, Jr. –Pediatrician: Died 1995

Dr. John Hume—Orthopedist: Died 2004

Dr. Thomas Calhoun—General Surgeon: Died 2003

Dr. Sheridan H. Settle—Ophthalmologist: Living

Dr. Calvin R. Dow, Jr. –Internist: Died 2004

Dr. Howard W. Kenny – Internist and Medical Director: Died 1996

Dr. Henry W. Foster, Jr. – Obstetrician/Gynecologist: Living

Mr. Louis A. Rabb was the Hospital Administrator.: Died 2015

It was during the time that I was there that the new hospital was built. The ground breaking ceremony took place the first month of my employment. Everyone was overjoyed. I did not get the sense of excitement that they had. Before I left, the new hospital was completed with an intercom system. I later learned that no provisions were made to handle the dirty linen. The planning committee had neglected to have a nurse-consultant to advise them on infection control and that soiled linen in a hospital has to be handled in a certain way. So, in the new hospital, linen baskets were seen all over the place for someone to take down to the basement to be washed. There was not a separate elevator for contaminated linen or trash. The same one used to transport patients was used for dirty linen. I was appalled that this big company out of New York, that Mr. Rabb had put so much faith in, had screwed the hospital and Tuskegee. No thought of infection control was put into the plans yet they purported to be experts at designing hospitals.

After graduating from Tuskegee Institute, my husband accepted a job with the Navy Yard in Philadelphia, Pennsylvania.

Part Four

Slavery and Discrimination in Health Care

Chapter 9

The Impact of Slavery on Health

In researching my family history using Ancestry.com. Family-search.com, census data, death certificates, birth certificates, and family papers, I have been able to identify only one ancestor that was documented a slave. Nathaniel Thompson, my great, great grandfather was the father to Iverson Thompson, my great grandfather. Nathaniel was listed as a slave on a slave schedule in 1840. His birth was calculated to have been in 1819. In the 1870 census he was listed as a farmer. That was only five years following the end of the Civil War. His sons were listed as farm laborers. I would imagine that this was the beginning of share cropping. I am still searching for information though the Freedmen's Bureau to find information about my great, great grandfather.

Through further research, I learned that slaves were provided medical care by the slave-holder. At times the slave-holder would put a doctor on contract for one year. The doctor was responsible for the slaves and the slave-holder's family. This occurred where there were many slaves. It was believed that many slaves relied on folk medicine before seeking care from the doctor. Depending on in what state the slave resided it was determined what kind of health care he/she received. It was felt that because the slave was the property of the slave-holder, he treated the slave just like he would his farm animals. After all, they were considered capital and a financial investment. Was this what slavery was like for my great, great grandfather? Following the

Civil War and during Reconstruction, freed slaves had no health insurance or any other method of paying for health services. (Savitt, Medicine and Slavery: The Diseases and Health Care of Blacks in Antebellun Virginia, 2002).

The diet of the enslaved was not of a nutritious nature. Pork and corn were the mainstays of the diet. There were few fresh vegetables. We now know the role of and the effect of a poor diet. Slaves often suffered from Scurvy, which is due to a deficiency of vitamin C in the diet. The other common condition was Rickets which is due to a deficiency of vitamin D. Because of these poor diets, there was a high infant mortality rate. Those children who survived had very low birth weights and we can imagine that the learning capacity was also affected. Yet, the whites wanted to say that "blacks" were lazy. They were not lazy. They were probably suffering from poor nutrition that affected their muscle development and strength as well as their learning abilities. Therefore, when a slave became ill, their immune systems were compromised already making their resistance to common illnesses and diseases insufficient. What impact did this have on their offspring? It's unfortunate that in the United States today, the poor are still suffering from poor nutrition and poor health care, both blacks and poor whites. (Fett, 2002)

Childhood poverty, children under the age of 18, in the year 2010 continued to be too high for a country as wealthy as the United States of America. Sixteen million children lived in households with income below 100 percent of the poverty threshold ($22,314 for a family of four). Some of these children's only full meal is the free lunch at school (mchb.jrsa.gov/chusa12/pc/pages/cp.html, 2013)

Slavery in West Virginia was a slightly different story. West Virginia was born out of the Civil War. Western Virginians would not support Virginia as a confederate state. They seceded from Virginia establishing a new state in 1863. The state's first constitution provided for slavery to be phased out. But it was not until 1865 following the 13th amendment that West Virginia abolished slavery. However, at the state's constitutional convention in 1872, blacks were guaranteed the right to vote, but it included a clause that "white and colored shall not be taught in the same school" and sanctioned a racially stratified and unequal society that would persist until the late twentieth century. (Alton Hornsby, 2011)

As the African American population increased, so did the racial hostility. In 1919, a white mob lynched two black coal miners at Chapmanville, Logan County, West Virginia. In the 1920s, chapters of the Ku Klux Klan (KKK) were formed in Logan, Mercer, and Kanawha counties. In 1918 three black men were elected to the state legislature: Charleston attorney, T.G. Nutter; Keystone attorney, Harry J. Capehart; and coal miner, John V. Coleman of Fayette County.

There were feeble attempts during Reconstruction to incorporate former slaves into mainstream society even giving them voting rights. The Freedman's Bureau made some of those feeble attempts by offering support in housing, land development, legal aid, and health care. Following the Civil War, Freedmen's Bureau was the first social welfare agency created to address the problems of freed slaves. It operated from 1865 to 1872. It was responsible for the establishment of Storer College in Harpers Ferry, West Virginia. What is unfortunate is the fact that President Andrew Johnson, who was a southerner, did not give the Freedman's Bureau enough time to allow the former slaves to get established. Once a people who had been enslaved for 400 years are given seven years to become established is absolutely ludicrous. He would not renew the program and felt that the former slaves would become dependent on the Federal government. So instead of support, there was destruction in its place. (staff, 2009)

Segregation was the abominable sin that destroyed the foundation of the United States of America. I have read many books that show how segregation destroyed African American family. It also destroyed the strength of the nation by preventing the development of ideas, inventions, political thought, and the establishment of strong health care programs and institutions.

Segregation in health care was the absolute worst. African American physicians were not permitted to receive clinical experience at white owned hospitals. African American women who became nurses were treated as indentured servants by both black and white physicians.

The African American population's health needs were neglected. Segregation forced African Americans to establish their own facilities for health care needs. This was accomplished by establishing black owned hospitals and nursing schools. Almost all were inferior to the white institutions. Most of the hospitals that were established by African Americans were done with the aid of white philanthropists whose desire it was to perpetuate segregation. At the time, many felt that these good white people had the interest of African Americans by establishing schools and hospitals. However, many black physicians as well as individuals such as W.E.B. Dubois, saw this as a perpetuation of segregation. (Gamble, 1995). After *Plessy vs Ferguson*, where the Supreme Court upheld segregation, promoting the "separate but equal" philosophy; which was and still is perpetuated and continues to be, there was no equality. Had it not been for the Civil Rights Act of 1965, we would still be experiencing this separate but equal philosophy.

Nursing for African American women was an abomination as well. As in the medical profession, African American women were undereducated, over worked, and under paid. The nursing schools were established as part of the black hospitals. Nurses were more maids than nurses performing such chores as cleaning, cooking, washing, and babysitting. They had no professional organization. It took many years to develop professional nursing schools and to establish formal clinical practice sites. There was not a real need for professional nurses until the black hospitals were established, especially those established by black physicians. They found a need for black nurses to care for their sick black patients. (Hine, Black Women in White: Racial Conflict and Cooperation in the Nursing Profession, 1860-1950, 1989)

Several hospitals were established by the Freedman's Bureau, however, only one still exists, Freedman's Hospital in Washington, D.C., now the Howard University Hospital.

Black physicians had a difficult time as well. Black men who wanted to become doctors had difficulty finding a medical school in the United States that was willing to train them. Some had the means to travel out of the country to places like France and Germany to be trained and then return to the United States. Also, because their secondary education was so limited, they often needed remedial training. During the Reconstruction period, Freedman Hospital was established. It would later affiliate with Howard University to establish a medical school. It along with Meharry Medical School which soon followed would become the leading medical school for black doctor's training and where graduates could practice clinical skills. As a consequence black physicians determined that they would have to establish facilities to educate and train black physicians. (Gamble, 1995) Their attempts came to naught because most failed due to lack of funds and support. Those that survived were financed by white philanthropists and other charitable organizations. Some black owned hospitals did survive and lasted for several years. There were few white hospitals willing to permit the students to gain clinical experience.

Health insurance was out of the question. Most medical care was received on a charitable basis. That is why most facilities failed.

PART FIVE

MARYLAND

Chapter 10

Home of Frederick Douglas

After graduating from Tuskegee Institute, my husband took a job with the Naval Engineering Department located on the Delaware River at its Navy yard. We moved to Drexel Hill, Pennsylvania, a suburb just outside of Philadelphia. We lived there for one year. During that year I became pregnant again with a six month old and a three year old running around the house. I had a spontaneous abortion and was hospitalized for two days in a hospital in Media, Pennsylvania. Prior to accepting the job in Pennsylvania, my husband had applied for a position with the Federal Government. He received a call from the Federal Power Commission (now Federal Energy Regulatory Commission: FERC) offering him a position in their utilities division after working in Pennsylvania for one year. He accepted and we moved back to the Washington Metropolitan Area, to the State of Maryland.

We began looking for an apartment in Maryland because the rent in the District of Columbia was outrageously high and continues to be so. In addition, we were leery of the school system. My husband began working before we moved from Pennsylvania. He lived with his oldest sister and would commute to Pennsylvania every other weekend. The other weekend I and the children would commute to Maryland for house hunting. We were unable to find a house, so we settled on an apartment. We had a 1972 Beetle Volkswagen. The drive to Maryland was fun except for a phobia I had of driving through tunnels. I drove around the Baltimore beltway instead of going through the Harbor Tunnel. That added an additional 45 minutes to an hour on to the trip.

We moved into an apartment in Hyattsville, Maryland. I got a job working with a Health Maintenance Organization (HMO), Group Health Association (GHA). We lived in Hyattsville for one year while we looked for a house. We would find our first home in Riverdale, Maryland. We lived there for five years before we learned that we were outgrowing the space.

While we were living there it became time for our daughter, who turned two years old, to have the first corrective surgery of a birth defect on her right hand. The surgery was performed by a renowned plastic surgeon, Dr. Gordon Letterman. The only complication she had was that a suture was left in the surgery site which became infected. It was eventually removed and her hand healed.

Our daughter was very athletic as soon as she could walk. She was a climber. She once climbed up on to the kitchen table and was eating out of the sugar bowl at the age of 8 months old. We bought her a Tyke Bike when we lived in Drexel Hill, Pennsylvania. There was a sloping sidewalk that led to the street. She found out that she could go to the top of the slope and ride without pushing herself with her feet. She would go to the top of the slope and give herself a big push and throw up both of her feet and go speeding down the hill. That was the beginning of her athletic career. She would later letter in track, basketball, and tennis while in high school.

It was during this time that I was beginning to become disillusioned with nursing. There were so many restrictions. Nurses could not make diagnoses, they could not use their brains to make suggestions on the care of patients. We were only allowed to make patient care plans. That was the limit of our knowledge base. Nurses were not included on the physician's rounds. As I looked for an alternative career, I recalled that when I was in Tuskegee Dr. Campbell had encouraged me to go to the University of Colorado where the initial Nurse Practitioner program was established. I located a program at Catholic University that offered a program for Pediatric Nurse Practitioners. At the time I was working in the Pediatric Department at

GHA. I decided that I did not want to be a Pediatric Nurse Practitioner. After wrestling with parents all day, I knew I did not want to remain in pediatrics. Too many parents were ignorant, uncontrollable, uneducated, and over-bearing. Many were hard headed and would not follow instructions. It was too frustrating. I continued to look. At some point, I found information about the Physician Assistant Program (PA).

I learned that Howard University in Washington, D.C., had such a program. I made an appointment with its Medical Director, Dr. Nadiry. I wanted to know exactly what the program offered and what would my capabilities be once completing it. I was surprised to learn that it trained you to perform some of the basic skills that the Nurse Practitioner program offered. The program was established initially for military corpsman who had great skills that were used in the military service but could not be used in civilian life. The program offered a certification and was opened to other health professionals. Nurses were one of those groups. I applied to the program and was accepted. The program was for 18 months. Mine was the fourth class to graduate from the Howard University program. My score on the National Certification Boards for Physician Assistants was the fourth highest from Howard University.

My first job as a PA was in a private practice with Dr. Melvin Gerald. He had a family practice and was a graduate from Howard University Medical School. The practice was a small one, so I felt I would get some good experience. Well, that was the wrong impression and a big mistake! The first thing that Dr. Gerald did was to fire the student nurse whom he had hired to perform EKGs and draw blood. He told me that since I was a nurse that I could take on the nurses' functions. In addition, he assigned me to all of the older women with multiple chronic health problems, some very complicated. He would see all of the young women with gynecological complaints. It did not take me long to find out this was not the place for me to work. For the first time in my working life, I quit a job without having another one to go to. After going to school to become a PA and have him determined that I would work as a nurse was defeating my whole purpose.

I was uncomfortable with the work setting. I would accept a positon at the American University Student Health Center. I was able to practice my newly acquired skills in this position.

During the Physician Assistant Program at Howard University, we were required to find a preceptor for our clinical experience. I remembered the physicians that I had worked with while nursing at GHA. One of those was Dr. Hardman, a pediatrician. The other was Dr. Dorothy Millon, an internist. While working at the American University Student Health Center, I received a telephone call from Dr. Millon. She told me that GHA was looking to hire some advanced practitioners (NPs and PAs had earned this new job classification). She said that she remembered me and was impressed by my skills. She also mentioned that the organization was attempting to diversify their staff. She encouraged me to apply for the position, which I did. I was hired and worked there for 12 years.

During my employment as a PA, there were many political issues in the professional organization. I attended several conventions sponsored by the National Associations for Physician Assistants. There was a lot of turmoil and bickering about the role of the PA; what their role should be, whether nurses should or could take orders from a PA, and whether physicians needed to sign off on all PA documentation. After leaving one convention, I determined that I wanted to work as a Nurse Practitioner where the lines were not so blurred. I wrote the American Nursing Association (ANA) and asked if the advance education that I had acquired at Howard University in their PA program would be acceptable to sit for the N.P. boards. They accepted my credentials from Howard and I sat for the national boards, passing and being certified as an Adult Nurse Practitioner in 1978. I worked for another 30 years as a nurse practitioner, retiring in 2008.

We moved to Prince George's County in 1978. It was a four bedroom house. The children enjoyed seeing the house being built. Both of the children were in elementary school and this is the place where they grew up.

CHAPTER 11

BIRTH DEFECT AND THE LAW

One day I was standing in line at the grocery store when our daughter was about nine years old. On the magazine rack was a copy of the National Enquirer with a picture of a child with a deformed hand. The headlines stated that this child's birth defect had been caused by Bendectin, a drug his mother had taken during pregnancy. I purchased the paper and brought it home to discuss with my husband. We decided not to pursue anything because this paper had a reputation of exaggerating the facts. We would later see the same subject in an article written in the Washington Post newspaper. That led us to believe that there was something that rang true to the story. We decided to seek an attorney, since I had taken the same drug during my pregnancy with our daughter and she was born with a defected right hand and arm. These were the type of birth defects that had been associated with this drug. We felt that if this was true, the drug should be taken off the market. This was the beginning of a fight with pharmaceutical companies for many years.

The attorney that responded to our request of seeking someone who dealt with medical malpractice and drug companies was attorney Barry Nace of the Paulson & Nace Law firm. The drug, Bendectin was developed and administered to pregnant women to control nausea and vomiting. Nausea and vomiting in pregnancy, commonly called "morning sickness," is a frequent occurrence in pregnant women. Studies have shown that at least 80% of pregnant women experience this event. In some women, the condition can become severe causing the woman to become dehydrated. This condition may warrant the treatment of intravenous fluids. When this occurs, the condition is called "hyperemesis gravidarum" or excessive vomiting in pregnancy. The vomiting usually occurs early in the first trimester or the first three months of pregnancy. The symptoms occur within the fourth and seventh week of pregnancy. I experienced the nausea and vomiting during both pregnancies. With my daughter, it appears that the vomiting started before I knew I was pregnant. (Staff, Diseases and Conditions : Morning Sickness, 2014)

Over the years many home remedies have been used to alleviate the nausea and vomiting. The cause of this event is still not known. Much research has been done to identify the cause. Some studies indicate that there is a hormone imbalance. Ginger is a common substance that has been used to relieve symptoms. It wasn't until Bendectin was developed that a drug was used to relieve these symptoms. The drug contained an antihistamine. Being in nursing, I was very familiar with this drug. It was the drug of choice for nausea and vomiting in pregnancy.

Our attorney went to Tuskegee, Alabama, to the pharmacy where my prescription had been filled, to find that the pharmacist had the original prescription filed in storage. He still had the first prescription that he filled in his pharmacy. The prescription identified that it was filled on my 42nd day of pregnancy. This was indeed a treasure. This is the critical time when the limbs are being developed in the fetus.

The pharmaceutical company "Merrill Dow" used every trick in the book to try to determine that it was anything but Bendectin that I took which caused our daughter's birth defect. I was 38 years old when we started this process. I was found to have developed uterine fibroids. The pharmaceutical company tried to say that the fibroids caused the birth defect, only to learn that I did not have fibroids when I was 29 years old, ten years younger when our daughter was born. Our expert witness, Dr. Alan Done, who was a board certified pediatrician and toxicologist, testified that research shows that Bendectin had tetragenic properties (known to cause birth defects of fetal limbs).

Much evidence was presented during our daughter's trial. After four weeks, a 12 member jury found in favor of our daughter. Merrill Dow withdrew the drug off of the market after the jury awarded our daughter $750,000. She has yet to receive one penny of that award. The unthinkable happened! The judge overturned the jury verdict and ruled in favor of the drug company. His excuse was that the information presented at trial was too scientific and technical for the people on the jury to understand and make a decision. Now, how often does that happen? We had two theories about that: (1) the judge was paid off by the pharmaceutical company and/or (2) the judge was prejudiced and could not or would not allow a black child and her family to win against a big pharmaceutical giant. Whatever the reason was, the outcome was ugly. The presiding judge is now dead. I pray that he asked God for forgiveness before he took his last breath.

The case went on for years. Our attorney appealed to the Supreme Court but the case was sent back to the lower courts. The final outcome was an opinion written by a law clerk not a judge. We were interviewed by many local television stations, the BBC, and appeared on the "Good Morning America" the morning television show where I was interviewed by Jane Pauley. The New York Times and the Washington Post wrote articles about our case as well as the National Enquirer.

Our attorney would go on to represent many other similar cases; some against Bendectin and other drugs. However, because of the national attention that our daughter's lawsuit drew, the pharmaceutical, Merrill Dow, was forced to withdraw Bendectin from the market. That was our ultimate goal. So we won! There is much more to the story, but that is another book.

After being off the market for 30 years, Bendectin has resurfaced with a new name, DICLEGIS. Its purpose is to alleviate pregnant women's suffering from nausea and vomiting. We shall see how soon the birth defects reappear.

CHAPTER 12

LIFE LONG LEARNING

I was still not happy with my work status and felt that something was missing. While working as an Adult Nurse Practitioner, I was painfully aware that I did not have a college degree. I had a diploma from nursing school and a certificate from Howard University. The American Nurses' Association had published a "white paper," which outlined the development of the nursing profession. One issue highlighted was the role of nurses who did not hold a bachelor's degree.

I learned that Bowie State College had developed a nursing program for nurses with diplomas who could earn their bachelor's degree. After being out of school for over 10 years, I felt this was the right time to go back to school to get my bachelor's degree in nursing. I enrolled in the program and for the next four years went to classes part-time while I worked as a manager supervising 40 employees and working as a nurse practitioner seeing clients at GHA.

I had already completed the training at Howard University as a physician's assistant and had passed both the Physician Assistant and Nurse Practitioner's National Certification Board examinations. I began taking classes part time in 1981. I was able to challenge several courses through examinations. I finally graduated Cum Laude in 1985 with a Bachelor of Science Degree in Nursing. I applied to Johns Hopkins School of Public Health and was accepted. I graduated with a Master's Degree in Health Policy and Management with emphasis on Occupational Health in 1986. I would have two memorable experiences while attending Johns Hopkins School of Public Health.

One morning as I entered the back door from the parking lot, the guard spoke to me in a very excited voice. He was almost screaming. He was saying, "The shuttle exploded!" When I was finally able to understand what he was shouting, I looked up at the small television screen that was attached to the wall above his desk to see the shuttle exploding. An eerie feeling went all over my body. My children had been so excited because a school teacher was aboard the shuttle. I would learn that Christa McAuliffe had attended Bowie State College to earn her Master's degree in Education. I would later work in the building on campus that was named in honor of her.

The second experience occurred one morning in October 1985 as I was driving to Baltimore. It was about 6 A.M. and had been raining, so it was not light yet. Suddenly I was hit, my car spun around, and I was hit again by a car behind me on the passenger's side of the car. I did not see what happened but later learned that a car traveling south towards Washington, D.C., crossed the median which was a grassy area a minimum of 100 feet between the north and south bound lanes of the Baltimore Washington Parkway. The accident occurred just past the Route 32 exit that goes to Fort Meade. I also learned that he had hit the car in front of me first and it was her car that hit me initially and then the car behind. My car was hit twice. The woman in the car in front of my car was taken away from the scene by ambulance. Her attorney contacted me for information. I could give none because I did not see what happened. Other motorists had to tell me what they saw. My car was towed from the scene of the accident. The park police were called and they took me to their headquarters in Greenbelt, Maryland. My husband came and picked me up. I drove him to work and then drove myself to school. When I got to Baltimore I could barely get out of the car. I was in so much pain with spasms in my neck, shoulders, and back, it was all I could do to walk to the hospital emergency room. I was examined, given some pain medication, and I went to class. That was a dumb thing to do looking back. But I did not want to miss any classes. I would eventually have to have physical therapy on my neck and back for 12 weeks. As a results of the injuries, the muscle in one side of my neck shortened causing me to have limited range of motion to my neck till this day. The driver of the car was a young man who was driving on suspended licenses, the car was not insured, and it had bad tags. He had many excuses for why he was on the highway. I went to his hearing only to see his punishment as a slap on the wrist. I guess that was because no one was killed.

While I was in college, both of my children were in high school. I had completed my education before they enrolled in college. My husband was a great support, although he did not understand why I wanted to go to school and why I didn't want to become a physician. I was convinced that God intended for me to be a nurse and the best nurse that I could be. Every place that I worked I feel that I made a difference. I wanted the hands-on care for my patients, whether I was just a registered nurse or an adult nurse practitioner. I wanted to spend time with patients teaching them how to care for themselves and their families. I wanted to see everyone who was in need of care to get that care. Even if it meant they were incarcerated.

I must say that I had a very satisfying career. Since being retired, I have continued to educate whenever possible. I write health articles for the church newsletter. I write faith articles during Lenten season and Advent season. I have had articles published in the Missionary magazine for the Women's Missionary Society of the African Methodist Episcopal Church and the Yearbook used for teaching local missionary societies.

I was well equipped to focus on wellness promotion. What I found working for the HMO was the ungrateful attitude that the patients exhibited. There was a lot of abuse in the utilization of services. At times, patients would tell me that they were paying my salary when they disagreed with my treatment plan. Most patients were angry when they did not leave the office with a prescription for an antibiotic in hand. When I explained that antibiotics were not effective in the treatment of viruses, they would look at me like I was out of my mind. They often stated that I had not done anything for them. I don't believe that much has changed since those days. Now we are seeing a lot of drug resistant strains of bacteria because of over use of antibi-otics. After seeing so many patients who had no health insurance and seeing the serious nature of their illnesses, I was provoked to see those who had health insurance feel so entitled and so ungrateful.

I would leave GHA and take a position as the coordinator of a research project, working with a company which had obtained a grant to monitor the impact of AZT, the first drug used to treat HIV and AIDS. The name of the company was Biospherics. It was here that research was being carried out to find an artificial sweetener. I worked for this company for one year before returning to the hospital setting as an occupational health nurse practitioner. I would work in this oc-cupation for 20 years. I would later take a positon working in the cor-rectional setting. That was an eye opener.

Some of the sickest patients I took care of during my entire nurs-ing career were those incarcerated inmates. These individuals in many cases were homeless or living on the fringes. Of course, the two facil-ities where I would work were located in the District of Columbia and Maryland, where the population was 85% African American males. The inmates were admitted with sexually transmitted infec-tions such as HIV/AIDS and Condyloma Acuminatum and Secondary Syphilis. Often, some had been under treatment but would stop and get restarted when they became incarcerated. This off and on medical regime is what creates the opportunity for drug resistant strains of or-ganisms. At least one third of the inmates had some mental health issue. The correctional facilities are no place for the mentally ill. However, since most mental health institutions closed there are few places for them to go. If they don't have health insurance that makes them more unlikely to get care. And if they are homeless, I would imagine they would not get Medicaid even if they qualified for it. So, they end up in the criminal justice system. We are just now seeing our politicians look at this issue seriously.

I would imagine this attention comes now that many whites are be-coming drug addicts and entering into the criminal justice system. There is also talk of lowering the sentencing for nonviolent drug offenses. Maybe the prison population will now become more homogenized.

CHAPTER 13

SPIRITUAL LIFE

My spiritual life began as a toddler at home. Mother would read Bible stories to all of us when we were small. That was something that we looked forward to on Sunday evening (before television). These Bible stories carried over into Sunday school. I remember at least three Sunday school teachers. Mrs. Bartley was my teacher in the primary department. Mrs. Bell was my junior teacher and Mrs. Rosa Motley was my intermediate girls teacher. I was an active member of the Baptist Youth Fellowship (BYF) because Mother was the director. I participated in all plays both during Easter and Christmas. We also held a Children's Day program. During the summer we had vacation Bible school. Church was an intricate part of my life.

After going to nursing school in Clarksburg, West Virginia, I found myself in Sunday school and would eventually become a co-teacher to Mr. E.B. Saunders who was the former principal to the Kelly Miller High School. The Water Street Baptist Church is where I met Rev. Henry Gregory. His father was the pastor. I also attended church with my roommate, Betty. She was a member of the United Methodist denomination. She had an aunt who lived near the Baptist church. The United Methodist was nearby. When she spent the weekend with her aunt, she would invite me to go to church with her. That was my first encounter with Methodism.

When I moved to Washington, D.C., I attended Shiloh Baptist Church on two occasions. On my first visit, I learned that Rev. Gregory, who was on the ministerial staff of Shiloh, was engaged. He would introduce me to his close friend, Pennington Greene. I eventually attended Metropolitan African Methodist Episcopal Church where I would spend the rest of my spiritual life as I and my family grew. Of course this church will always hold a special place in my heart because it was there that I met my husband. I prayed that God would send a good man in my life when the time was right. Of course I would date several men before I met my husband, but it was not in God's plan for me to connect with them. We became members of Metropolitan AME Church when our son, Terry Lee, was baptized in 1968.

I became a Sunday school teacher for the Primary department. I later taught senior high school students. I held this position for ten years. All of those young people are now adults with children of their own. I see several of them from time to time and am very proud to see them on their spiritual journeys. Two of my students were Robin DeVeaux and her brother David, who were children of our pastor at that time, Rev. William P. DeVeaux. David would become a preacher. Their father was the pastor of Metropolitan African Methodist Episcopal Church for 13 years and would be elected as a Bishop following his pastoral service at Metropolitan.

I joined the missionary society in 1988 and Church Women United in 1989. The pastor's wife, Patricia Ann Morris DeVeaux, was the president of the missionary society and I was the secretary under her administration for eight years.

As I continued to grow I found myself reading the Bible more. I would eventually read the entire Bible three times, one edition of the King James Version, the New International version, and the Archaeological Study Bible, the NIV version. As a participant of the Christian Education Department I began contributing articles to both the Advent and Lenten bulletins. As I go back and read some of these articles I can see my growth.

Over the years I have tried to put my spiritual life into practice. I have tried not to be judgmental, however, when it comes to politics I cannot not help but to make strong judgmental comments on injustice as I have seen and am seeing.

The Republican Party has had a tendency to lean towards the Evangelical denomination. It appears this group of individuals are supposed to have something special to offer politicians than other denominations. I wondered what it is? My take is that Evangelicals are made of "Bible toting angry white men". These are the individuals who want African Americans to go back to Africa. They appear to feel that the Civil Rights Act of 1965 gave African Americans too much authority. They are against allowing people of color the right to vote. Look what happened! An African American was elected president of the United States of America. That should not have happened. Well, what can we do about that? Don't give him the honor of recognizing him as the president. First of all he is not an American because he was born in "Kenya" and second, he is a Muslim. The hypocrisy continued through President Barack Obama's **two terms.** Of course that was not supposed to happen either. He was not going to be elected a second term. That was Mitch McConnell's promise to America. The Republicans set their goal during his first administration to block every policy he offered. That would make him look like he was a failed president. God had other plans for him.

Richard Wolfe wrote an article in "The Guardian" newspaper on August 9, 2016 that describes perfectly how the Republican Congress efforts to destroy President Obama, destroyed the Republican Party, and created a monster by the name, Donald Trump. The title of the article was *"The Republicans tried to sink Obama. Instead, the party imploded"*.

The Evangelicals don't believe in abortions nor birth control. It is not because it's wrong or a sin; it's because the white race is becoming a minority. If it were only African American and Hispanic women having abortions it certainly would not be an issue. However, there are more white women having abortions than African Americans and Hispanics. So now we must defund Planned Parenthood as well. The sad part is the Republicans who are against Planned Parenthood believe they only perform abortions, which is so far from the truth. They actually provide more healthcare services for women, especially screening for cancer (Pap smear) and other preventive services. They also screen for and treat sexually transmitted infections. I have referred many women to Planned Parenthood and it was not for an abortion. It was because they could get affordable health care services there. The Republicans are so fixed on remaining the superior race so their numbers must be higher. There is nothing godly about being an Evangelical. Yet, our political leaders rely on them to get elected.

As I interpret the Bible, I have made an analogy of the Pharisees to the member of our Christian Congressmen. In the New Testament the Pharisees are described as being meticulous observers of obligation under the Law for purity, tithing, and Sabbath observances; and their emphasis was on *oral law* as equally binding to the Law. The Pharisees became hypocritical because in attempting to be faithful to the letter of the Law, they lost the spirit of the Law. "The Pharisees were primarily not a political party but a society of scholars and pietists. They enjoyed a large popular following and in the New Testament they appear as spokesmen for the majority of the population." (www.britannica.com/print/topic/455129, 2015).

The New Testament illustrates the conflict between the Pharisees and Jesus Christ. (Matthew, Chapter 23 Scribes and Pharisees). "The Pharisees and the teachers are experts in the Law of Moses. So obey everything they teach you, but don't do as they do. After all, they say one thing and do something else. They piled heavy burdens on people's shoulders and won't lift a finger to help. You Pharisees and teachers of the Law of Moses are in trouble! You're nothing but show-offs. You travel over land and sea to win one follower. And when you have done so, you make that person twice as fit for hell as you are. You wash the outside of your cups and saucers, while on the inside there is nothing but grit (greed) and grime (selfishness). Outside you look good, but inside you are evil and only pretend to be good." (Jesus Condemns the Pharusees and the Teachers of the Law of Moses)

This same behavior is seen in our elected officials in Congress, who are wedded to the Constitution (the Law). They too have become hypocritical in attempting to use the Law for what it was not intended. Voting is a good example. States are now drafting new laws to usurp the Constitution and prevent people of color from voting. All African Americans know that when the Constitution was written, it was mainly intended for the ruling class of white people, but not all white people. The poor white were not included. The 13th, 14th, and 15th Amendments were added to the Constitution in order that African Americans would be included.

Our first African American President, Barack Obama, was accused of breaking the (Law) Constitution (nevermind the fact that he is an attorney by profession and taught Constitutional Law at Harvard University). He had to resort to using his Constitutional authority because the Pharisees (Representatives and Senators) were hypocrites who refuse to abide by the Constitution in performing their duties as Congressmen. The only part of the Constitution that they feel strongly about is the Second Amendment- the right to bear arms. This is unfortunate because when the Constitution was written, there was no Militia, i.e. no formal army or military. Therefore, the farmers and ordinary citizens had to bear arms to protect themselves from the British and the Native Americans. Now, we have a military that protects the country from foreign invasions and police to protect the citizens. So why do citizens need to be armed? The National Rifle Association (NRA) has become the conscience of our Congressmen and women. Guns are not purchased to hunt food for livelihood, they are purchased to "protect one's self". We all know that is "Bull". Guns are made to kill people. That is the simple fact. What about those families whose loved ones have been massacred by madmen who had the ability to purchase a gun. Congress is spineless by not passing legislation that protect citizens from these horrors and they have no problem taking health care away from their constituents, whose best interest they are supposed to be representing.

The main issue that I have with Congress is their willingness to take away healthcare that was legislated into being by President Barack Obama's administration. To allege to be Christians, our Congress has done everything in its power to undo almost everything that the Black President has accomplished. The greatest accomplishment was the **Patient Protection and Affordable Care Act** which was shortened to the Affordable Care Act or ACA. It was nick-named "Obamacare" by the Republican party in an effort to taint the program. For hundreds of years those on the fringes of society, the poor and people of color, have been denied health insurance and affordable health care coverage. Since Reconstruction, many African Americans have been denied health care coverage because of lack of employment or working part-time jobs that offer no insurance. In the rural South, many African Americans are still caught up in the "share-cropper" system. Working at John A. Andrew Hospital in Tuskegee, Alabama, opened my eyes to the terrible state of health in the southern poor. To deny health care to American citizens is sinful. The United States of America is the richest country in the world, and yet we have people and babies starving and people without the benefit of healthcare. To know that there are elected officials who represent these poor individuals and would begrudge them from having health insurance so they that can get health care is unthinkable. And to know that Congressmen and women have the best healthcare in the world. It would be nice if the law was changed so that they would only be eligible for the same health insurance as all other Federal Government employees and citizens of the United States.

As an active participant in the health-care profession, I would often provide opportunities to members of our congregation when I became aware of a benefit that was free. On one of those occasions, I learned that the Health Department in the District of Columbia had obtained a grant for African American women to get free mammograms. I obtained 25 vouchers. The participant would call the Howard University Hospital to schedule an appointment for a free mammogram. I made verbal announcement at the church services on Sunday morning and put an announcement in the church bulletin. It ran for one month. I had the vouchers for 12 weeks. I could only give **one** voucher away. One church member approached me asking for a voucher after I had returned the remaining vouchers back into the Health Department. I told her she was too late. Soon after that she learned that she had breast cancer. I cannot understand why the women decline to accept the opportunity for free breast cancer screening. The women were too ashamed to admit that they were uninsured or too ashamed to admit that they were poor. Pride has killed many. I learned that some of the women only had Medicaid health care coverage and others had no health insurance. It blew my mind to see African American women neglect themselves. I have continued to share health information to the congregation through our quarterly newsletter.

We have seen the entrance of the 45th president of the United States, Donald Trump. His first goal was to join the Republican's band wagon to abolish the Affordable Health Care Act. Nevermind that there is nothing that the Republicans have developed to replace it. Why should he care? He was born wealthy so health care was not an issue for him. The only poor people he has had to deal with are probably his servants/employees. Does he offer them health care benefits? It would be good to know.

We have seen the people that Donald Trump has surrounded himself with in the White House. It is the pit of Hell. Satan has Donald Trump in the palm of his hand and is laying down screaming with delight because "The Donald" has surrounded himself with Satan's army. Oh! What a disaster for this country. When he gets through destroying as much as he is allowed to do before he is impeached, it will take decades to clean up the mess. People of all religions are praying that God put a stop to his shenanigans before it's too late.

I pray that the Congressmen and women who voted against the Affordable Health Care Act, (because it was created by a Black President) that will take health care away from millions of the poor and disinherited and give more money to the rich, will ask for God's forgiveness. Especially, one Mitch McConnell who swore that he was going to spend the first four years of President Barack Obama's administration trying to prevent him from being elected to a second term. I asked the question, who does Mitch McConnell represent? Was it only wealthy white men (his campaign donors)? What about all of the poor people who voted for him in Kentucky?

Yes, I pray that God will forgive me for being judgmental. He understands and knows the hearts of those who would speak out for justice.

CHAPTER 14

MOTHER'S HEART

As a child, Mother developed Rheumatic Fever. Of course, my grandparents believed in self-treatment. This was mainly because they did not have the money to seek medical care from the black physicians. There was no such thing as health insurance. Therefore, Granny treated Mother with home remedies. Little did she know how serious the illness was that she was treating. Rheumatic Fever is a complication from untreated "Strep Throat." The bacteria, streptococcus, attacks the heart valves causing damage. Mother did not learn that she had the condition until she was an adult. Granny told her that she was weak and should take care of herself by keeping her body warm and dry at all times. Mother was the youngest of six children and one of four girls. She was the only girl that had children. Her health remained good throughout her adult life except for her teeth, which she eventually had to have pulled for lack of dental care and tooth decay.

Mother was the only one of her parent's children who went to college. She graduated from Stratton High School in 1937 and attended West Virginia State University (formerly Institute) for two years. For some reason which we will never know, she eloped with my father in June 1940 instead of going back to college. I am sure that was a decision that she would live to regret for the rest of her life. Her famous saying to us was "you must go to school and get an education so that you can be independent."

Even with two years of college, Mother worked as a domestic while her children were growing up. She eventually got a position as a receptionist in a medical group practice where she worked for several years until someone decided she was too old and she was terminated. That was grounds for a lawsuit. Mother was very active in the NAACP and knew much about discrimination, both racial and age. She sued the company and won. Her final job before retiring was as a clerk at the county library. She was an avid reader. She loved that job and worked there until she was 78 years old.

One day she called me saying that her primary physician had referred her to a cardiologist in Charleston, West Virginia. She had had several episodes of Congestive Heart Failure and the physician told her that her heart could not take another one. I went home and took her to the physician in Charleston. He told us that she needed her heart valves replaced. The physician suggested that she have it done there. When we went home we had conversation with my other siblings. I did not trust the care of physicians in West Virginia. So that was out of the question. Referring her to an out-of-state facility was not going to work either. When I got back to Maryland, I reached out to some physicians that I had worked with in the past. I contacted Dr. Susan Liebenhaut, who was an internist that I had worked with at Group Health Association. She was in private practice. She referred me to the Heart Center at the Washington Hospital Center in Washington, D.C.

Since me and my sisters were still working, we felt that Mother needed to be near one of us following her recovery period. So, I got an appointment at the Heart Center and brought Mother there to be seen. She would eventually have the valve replacement surgery at the age of 79 years old. The physician showed me her heart on the echocardiogram. It was huge. She tolerated the surgery very well and her recovery went well also. I brought her home to live with me following her surgery. She lived with me from October 1997 until March 1998 when I took her back to West Virginia. The following year she was able to plant her vegetable garden again.

She experienced 10 wonderful years of good health until 2007 when she experienced a dissection of her aorta. The healthy heart valves, subsequently, were too strong for the muscles in her aorta causing stress and eventually a tear. I brought her back to Washington Hospital Heart Center where she saw the same cardiologist who treated her 10 years earlier. The news was not good. She would need major surgery in order to repair the tear. This time she was 89 years old. Mother and her children decided the risk of surgery was too great. She did not have the surgery. The condition became stable and she was taken back to West Virginia where she did well until 2009 when she experienced a second tear. That was her demise. She died from hemorrhage in July 2009 at the age of 90 years old. Had she lived she would have been 91 on August 30th.

Following Mother throughout her episodes of illnesses was a blessing for me. My education and experience as a registered nurse and nurse practitioner enabled me to make good clinical decisions for her treatments which prolonged her life. I count it a blessing from Almighty God that I was prepared to do so.

Mother sacrificed, worked very hard, and gave all her energy and encouragement to her children to get an education so that we could be self-sufficient and independent.

Fortunately for Mother, Medicare was available for her for medical coverage. My brother Dwight paid a premium for additional insurance called "Medigap." With the two insurances she was able to have hospitalization coverage and was not bankrupted because of her medical expenses. Without them she would have lost her house, all of her savings, and become a ward of the state/homeless. So many elderly individuals are not so lucky. Mother's only source of income was social security. She was very resourceful and frugal. So she did have a few pennies saved. Once our youngest brother left home to go to school, she never had to depend on Welfare again. The Affordable Health Care Act had not passed before she died.

The Republican Party would make things much more difficult for the elderly. Putting Social Security into a private fund would destroy many lives. I would expect the fund to face bankruptcy sooner under such a plan than for its management by the Federal Government.

The Senators and Congressmen have the best health benefits and coverage in the world. Yet, they would begrudge the poor and elderly from having the bare minimum. It is a tragedy! The United States of America is the richest country in the world and for individuals to lose everything because of illnesses and medical services is unthinkable.

CHAPTER 15

BILL'S LIVER

My husband worked in the Federal Government for 32 years after going back to Tuskegee University (formerly Institute) in Alabama to get his Bachelor of Science degree in Electrical Engineering. He retired in 2005.

That same year my oldest sister, Margaret, was diagnosed for the second time with breast cancer. She received the diagnosis in August and died in December. She had initially been diagnosed with breast cancer 10 years earlier. Her physician informed her that she had the kind of breast cancer that was likely to reoccur. It was recommended that she have the other breast removed. After the first five years she was again advised it would be a good idea to have the other breast removed. I talked to my sister and could not convince her that having her breast removed would probably prolong her life. Psychologically she could not see herself without any breast. So the second diagnosis was the end. I had just transferred onto the campus of Bowie State University to take the position of Director of Student Health Services. Prior to the transfer, I had operated a stand-alone nurse-managed clinic for the university in a public housing apartment unit for two years through a HUD grant. My sister was living in Oak Ridge, Tennessee. On Thanksgiving Day we traveled to Oak Ridge to see her hospitalized and doing poorly. That was the first time I had to take leave from a new job. She died on December 19th, so we had to travel back there for her funeral. She was buried in Beckley, West Virginia.

My husband had an accident in September 2006 when he fell off a ladder at 7 ft. from the roof. He was on a ladder washing windows. The fall fractured his spine in three places. The worst was a compression fracture (at lumbar vertebrae number 5 and sacral vertebrae number 1) or of L5 and S1. He was hospitalized for one week and came home in a "straight jacket." He remained upstairs for two weeks before he could handle the steps to come downstairs for his meals. His older sister came over every day and stay with him while I went to work. His recovery took one year, however after six months, he began substitute teaching in the local high schools teaching science and mathematics classes. That lasted until he became deathly ill from liver failure.

He was diagnosed with Primary Sclerosis Cholangitis many years ago and was told that he would eventually need a liver transplant. The illness came on suddenly in May of 2010, one year following the death of my mother. He was jaundiced, his legs and feet were grossly swollen, and he lost his appetite, lost weight, and was very lethargic. He was becoming confused and had begun planning for his death. When the physicians saw him at Washington Hospital Center, they were aware of the liver failure but also concerned about his gallbladder. He was a risk for hemorrhaging because his bleeding and clotting tests were too high. He would eventually be sent to the Hospital of the University of Pennsylvania where he was evaluated as a candidate for liver transplant. He was 70 years old. The physicians did not believe that he was 70 years old because his muscle tone was so good. That was because of him working in the garden for the last 20 years and eating truly organic vegetables. I retired in 2008 and took care of my mother from January 2009 until she died in July. Now, I was taking care of a very sick spouse. My nursing career was taking a new turn.

We had gone to Atlanta, Georgia, to visit my brother for the Memorial Day weekend. He wanted all of the family to be together for the first time since our mother's death. We had initially planned to drive to Atlanta, but Bill was not feeling well, so at the last minute we decided to take the train. I did not feel like doing the drive alone. We were unable to get a sleeper. The ride down to Atlanta from Washington, D.C., was not too bad. We were able to have two separate seats alone. Bill was able to stretch his legs out. While we were in Atlanta, Bill did not feel well and did not leave my brother's house the entire weekend. On our way back to Washington, the train was full to capacity. We boarded at 9:00 P.M. A baby cried all the way from Atlanta to Washington, D.C. We had to share a seat and Bill could not elevate his feet and legs. When we arrived at New Carrollton, where our daughter had left her car for us, my husband's feet were so swollen he could barely get his shoes on. During the next weeks, he became jaundiced, his feet and legs were so swollen that his skin was shining, and it looked like it was going to split. He had no appetite and was dragging around the house. The physicians determined that he qualified for a liver transplant. So he was placed on the waiting list. We were advised that the Hospital of the University of Pennsylvania would be the place where the surgery would take place. On August 4th at 11 A.M. we received a telephone call from the hospital that they had a liver. They want him at the hospital as soon as possible. We were on the next train to Philadelphia arriving at the hospital at 2 P.M. We waited and waited and waited for someone to come and take Bill upstairs. The Admitting Department was not expecting him. We told them that we had received a call to report to the hospital because they had a liver for him. When someone from the transplant team showed up two hours later, we were told that there had been a liver and the recipient had initially said he did not want the transplant, but he changed his mind so that it had to go to him. Bill was the next person in line for the liver. That was a great disappointment. We went back to the train station and back to Maryland. We were home by 9 P.M. that evening.

While he was waiting for a liver he developed Pneumonia. He developed a cough and fever. Off we went to the doctor's office where he was treated with intravenous antibiotics and released on oral antibiotics. The liver disease continued to be a challenge. He was seen and treated at Washington Hospital Center at least twice for fever and Vitamin K treatments. We received **the call** on a Wednesday, September 14, 2010, at 9:00 P.M. We arrived at the hospital in Philadelphia at 1 A.M. This time there was no train ride. I had to drive us there. That was the first time that I used the GPS, which was a blessing. It got me to the front door of the hospital. The hospital transplant team was waiting for us. Bill was taken into surgery at 6 A.M. and came out at 3 P.M. The surgeon told me that his gallbladder was cancerous. That was a surprise that no one had expected. However, out of 4 lymph nodes extracted during surgery only one was hot (had cancer cells). We were later told that if the physicians had known that his gallbladder was cancerous he would never have been approved for a liver transplant. You see God is always in the plan. It was his will that my husband get the transplant and that particular liver.

My husband was never able to take chemotherapy, because of his new liver. Three months after the transplant, he received his first dose of chemotherapy and he had a reactions to it. He did very well until during one of the visits to Philadelphia when he had a PET scan for follow up for the gallbladder cancer which showed some nodules in his lungs. They turned out to be Cryptococcus pneumonia. This is a fungal infection of the lungs common when the immune system has been suppressed. The immunosuppressant medicine that he had to take to prevent the body from rejecting the liver had created the perfect conditions for this organism to become active in the lungs. He would now be followed by an infectious disease specialist for two years and on medicine for this infection in addition to the other medications to prevent liver rejection.

One year following the transplant surgery he developed an incisional hernia which had to be surgically repaired. That was done local avoiding travel to Philadelphia. It has been five years and Bill is doing well. He must take several anti-rejection drugs as well as medicine for his Primary Sclerosing Cholangitis. He still has the disease that caused his liver to fail. Hopefully, this liver will last another 70 years. He is back to his gardening.

CONCLUSION

THE RICHEST COUNTRY IN THE WORLD

Fortunately for my family, we have good health insurance. What will tomorrow bring? Only God knows. When the Republicans finish screwing up the Affordable Health Care Act which affect every American except the Congressmen and women what will happen to the poor and uninsured? Who cares? I don't think it will be Mitch McConnell or Paul Ryan the current leaders of the Senate and House of Representatives respectively. The new president of the United States, Donald Trump, wants to make America great again. I hear him saying that he wants to take us back to the time before Medicaid and Medicare. His plan is to destroy the Affordable Health Care Act and take us back to the time when the KKK were terrorizing American citizens. God Bless the United States of America!!!

What is so unfortunate is that the men and women in the House of Representatives and the Senators forget why they were elected. . It has becomes a power thing. They forget the constituents and fight among themselves for what they want, not what the citizens of the United States need. They pander to the lobbyist and the wealthy. They are there to oversee what is best for the country not to promote their own self -interest and their selfish ideologies. Some of these men and women claim to be Christians. Yet their behavior demonstrate something more demonic.

I watched on television while Michele Bachman, the former congresswoman from Minnesota, ranted and raved about the ACA. She said there were "death panels" and that the insurance was going to "kill people"! What does she have to say after millions of Americans obtained health insurance for the first time; that the ACA has saved lives? What is her advice to her former colleagues? Is she their cheerleader, jumping up and down on the sideline encouraging them to REPEAL AND REPLACE the ACA?

Those of us who have worked and are still working in the healthcare profession will continue to see citizens die needlessly for lack of health insurance. We will see more babies starving. Can you believe this in the richest country in the world that we have one of the highest infant mortality rate than any comparable country? That the U.S has the highest rate of maternal mortality among high income countries? That 45,000 people die each year simply because they have no health insurance? (Health Care in the United States, 2009). What a sad commentary.

THE END

References

Abuse, N. C. (2010). *Statistics/Data*. Washington. DC: Administration on Aging: http://www.ncea.aoa.gov/Library/Data.

AFL-CIO, J. L. (2017). *John L Lewis*. Retrieved from hhtps://aflcio. org/about/history/labor/people/john-lewis.

Alton Hornsby, J. (2011). *Black America: A State-by-State Historical Encyclopedia*. Santa Barbara, California; Denver, Colorado; Oxford, England: Greenwood.

Anthony, M. K. (1867-1891). *Storer College, Brief- Historical-Sketch*. Harper's Ferry, W.VA: Morning Star Publishing House.

Bickley, A. R. (2006). *2006-2017 West Virginia Encyclopedia; Carter G. Woodson*.

census, R. C. (2014-2010). *quickfacts.census.gov/qfd/states/54/54081.html*. Retrieved from Raleigh County, West Virginia.

contributors, W. (22017, April 25). *Margarine*. Retrieved from Wikipedia, The Free Encyclopedia.

Covey, H. C. (1989). *African American Slave Medicine: Herbal and Non-Herbal Treatments*. Lanham * Boulder * New York * Toronto * Plymouth, UK: Rowman & Littlefirld Publisher, Inc.

Doctors and Dentists: Raleigh Co. Well Staffed with Physicians and Dentists. (n.d.). Retrieved from http:www.wvgenweb.org/ raleigh/black/ doctors.htm.

Eugene Dibble, J., & Louis A Rabb, R. B. (1961, March). Journal of the National Medical Association. *Original Communications*, pp. Vol 53- No 2.

Fett, S. M. (2002). *Working Cures: Healing, Health, and Power on South-*

ern Slave Plantations. Chapel Hill and London: The University of North Carolina Press.

Fishback, P. V. (Dec. 1986). Did Coal Miners "Owe Their Souls to the Company Store"? Theory and Evidence from the Early 1900s. *The Journal of Economic History, Vol. 46, No. 4,* 1011-1029.

Gamble, V. N. (1995). *Making a Place for Ourselved: The Black Hospital Movement 1920-1945.* New York, Oxford: Oxford University Press.

Hall, J., & Crosby, D. L. (2016). *Elder Abuse Surveillance: Uniform Definitions and Recommended Core Data Elements.* Retrieved from Center for Disease Control and Prevention/ National Ctr. for Injury Prevention Control.

Harlan, L. R. (1971, January). *West Virginia Historu, Booker T. Washington's West VA Boyhood pg 63-85.* Retrieved from www.wvculture.org/history/journal_wvh/wvh32-1html.

Haught, J. A. (1971, January). *West Virginia History: Institute: It Springs from Epic Love Story Vol 32 Number 2 PP 101-107.* Retrieved from http://www.wvculture.org/history/journal_weh/wvh32-2a.html.

Haymond, H. (1910). *History of Clarksburg, WV.* Retrieved from http:/genealogytrails.com/wva/harrison/clarksburg.html.

Health Care in the United States. (2009). Retrieved from www.nesri.org/programs/health-care-in-the-United-States.

Henry W Foster, J. M. (1997). *Make a Difference.* New York: Scribner.

Hine, D. C. (1989). *Black Women in White: Racial Conflict and Cooperation in the Nursing Profession 1890-1950.* Indianapolis: Indiana University Press.

Hine, D. C. (1989). *Black Women in White: Racial Conflict and Cooperation in the Nursing Profession, 1860-1950.* Blooming and Indianapolis: Indiana University Press.

I.W.W, P. b. (1922). *Coal-Mine Workers and Their Industry/ An Industrial Handbook.* Chicago, Illinois: The Industrial Workers of the World.

Jesus Condemns the Pharusees and the Teachers of the Law of Moses. (n.d.). In Matthew, *Bible* (p. Chapter 23 verses 2; 4;615;25;27).

Contemporary English Version.

Joe William Trotter, J. (1990). *Coal, Class and Color: Blacks in Southern West Virginia, 1915-32.* Chicago: University of Illinois Press.

Jones, J. H. (1981). *Bad Blood: The Tuskegee Syphilis Experiment.* New York, London, Toronto, Sydney: The Free Press.

Matthew. (n.d.). *Chapter 23 Scribes and Pharisees.* Holy Bible.

McClure, G. (Letter to the editor 1916). *jeff560.tripod.com/beckley2. html.* Retrieved from History of Beckley and Raleigh County.

McClure, G. T. (1916). *History of Beckley and Raleigh County.* Beckley: Raleigh Herald.

mchb.jrsa.gov/chusa12/pc/pages/cp.html. (2013). Retrieved from Children in Poverty Child Health USA 2012.

Meraji, S. M. (2013, October 18). *The Whitest Historically Black College in America.* Retrieved from http:www.npr.org/section/code switch/2013/10/18/236345546/the whitest-historically -black-college- in- america.

Morais, H. M. (1967). Fighting Back: Breakthrough at Tuskegee and Harlem. In H. M. Morais, *The History of the Negro in Medicine* (pp. 113-114). New York, Washington, London: Publishers Company, Inc.

Perry, E. S. (n.d.). *History of Toms Creek.* Retrieved from http://home-pages.rootsweb.ancestry.com/-duncanrw/tomscreek_camp.html.

Project, A. P. (2013). Post Tagged'poverty rate". Alabama, United States of America.

Raleigh County Quick Facts from the US Census Bureau. (n.d.). Retrieved from http://quickfacts.census.gov/qfs/states/54/54081.html.

Resouces, W. V. (2000 to 2012). 2012 West Virginia State Health Profile: Shaping safe and healthy communities. Harrison County, West Virginia, US.

Savitt, T. L. (1981). *Medicine and Slavery: The Diseases and Health Care of Blacks in Antebellum Virginia.* Urbana and Chicago: University of Illinois Press.

Savitt, T. L. (2002). *Medicine and Slavery: The Diseases and Health Care of Blacks in Antebellun Virginia.* University of Illinois Press.

Shepard, G. E. (2007). *West Virginia Mining Accidents: 1887-1927.*

Skloot, R. (2010). *The Immortal Life of Henrietta Lacks.* New York: Broadway Books of Random House.

staff, H. (2009). *March 03, 1865: Freedman's Bureau created.* Retrieved from http://www.history.com/this-day-in-history/freedmans-bureau

Staff, M. C. (2014). *Diseases and Conditions : Morning Sickness.* Retrieved from Mayo Clinic: http://mayoclinic.org/diseases-conditions/morning sickness/basics/definition/con-20033445?p=1

Staff, M. C. (2014). *Diseases and Conditions: Hydrocele.* Retrieved from http://mayoclinic.org/diseases-conditions/hydrocele/basics/definition/con-20024139.

Thomas J. Ward, J. (2003). *Black Physicians in the Jim Crow South.* Fayetteville: The University of Arkansas Press.

Washington, H. A. (2006). *Medical Apartheid: The Dark History of Medical Experimentation on Black Americans from Colonial Times to the Present.* New York: Anchor, A Division of Random House, Inc.

Wikipedia. (2011). *Mcdowell County, West Virginia.* Retrieved from http:en.wikipedia.org/w/index.title=McDowell_county,_West_Virginia.

Wikipedia. (2015). *City of St. Jude.* Retrieved from http://en.wikipedia.org/wiki/City_of_St_Jude.

Wikipedia. (2015). *John Albion Andrew.* Retrieved from http://en.wikipedia.org/w/index.php?title=John_Albion_Andrew&printable=yes.

Wikipedia. (2017). *Bluefield State College.* Retrieved from Wikipedia.

Williams, P. (1932). The Purchase of Medical through Fixed Periodic Payment. *National Bureau of Economic Research*, 165-192. Retrieved from http://www.nber.org/books/will32-1.

Wilson, J. F. (2006). *Coal Mine Scrip.* Retrieved from http://www.rootsweb.ancestry.com/-kyperry3/Scripts_by_Freddie.html.

www.britannica.com/print/topic/455129. (2015). *Pharisees.* Online Encyclopedia Britannica.